James B. Cregg is the new Dean of Optometry at the Los Angeles College of Optometry and received his master in ... in Los Angeles. He received a B.S. in Business Administration and a Degree in Optometry from The Ohio State University, and his O.D. from the Los Angeles College of Optometry. Former Director of Education for the Vision Conservation Institute, Dr. Cregg is a member of the American Optometric Association and Past President of both the California Optometric Association and the Los Angeles County Optometric Association. In addition to many articles both for the professional journals and for laymen, he is the author of several books, including The Story of Eyes ... published by The Herald Press Company.

JAMES R. GREGG is Professor of Optometry at the Los Angeles College of Optometry and an optometrist in private practice in Los Angeles. He received a B.S. in Business Administration and a Degree in Optometry from The Ohio State University, and his O.D. from the Los Angeles College of Optometry. Former Director of Education for the Vision Conservation Institute, Dr. Gregg is a member of the American Optometric Association and Past President of both the California Optometric Association and the Los Angeles County Optometric Association. In addition to many articles both for the professional journals and for laymen, he is the author of several books, including *The Story of Optometry* published by The Ronald Press Company.

EXPERIMENTS IN VISUAL SCIENCE

For Home and School

JAMES R. GREGG, O.D.

LOS ANGELES COLLEGE OF OPTOMETRY

Illustrations by

Bernice K. Gregg

THE RONALD PRESS COMPANY · NEW YORK

Library of Congress Catalog Card Number: 66–12385
PRINTED IN THE UNITED STATES OF AMERICA

Preface

There is no more fascinating realm of science than that which deals with the function of vision. It is a subject of profound significance to every individual. Yet, there is little material available to aid the young science student (or his teacher) in exploring the science of vision in a way he can thoroughly understand and enjoy. Conventional textbooks are too complicated; most of the beginning science books that touch on vision and optics at all are too elementary. There has been nothing to lead the student into physiological optics as the optometrist knows it.

The material in this book represents many levels of interest. Some of the experiments are elementary; yet, they will attract everyone, even adults, because they deal with the miracles of vision. On the other hand, some experiments involve highly theoretical concepts that will challenge the advanced student. Youngsters in the upper elementary grades can do many of the experiments; junior high and high school students will find them all stimulating, particularly the more advanced ones. Teachers can use much of the material for classroom demonstrations and as teaching aids. Some of the experiments are particularly adaptable as exhibits at science fairs.

Most of all, these experiments are intended to be fun! Inquisitive minds will find them especially entertaining.

Not all of the answers are in this book. In some cases, the explanations of the phenomena observed are still being sought. The experimenter must use his imagination; he may want to search out other books and references to expand his knowledge. Some of the mysteries surrounding the function of vision will be solved, perhaps, by someone reading this book. There is a broad field for those who might wish to pursue a career in visual science.

Pure researchers will be needed to delve into the basic questions of how the visual process works. Applied scientists must determine how the known facts can be used to improve human performance. Then, too, the demand for teachers will increase—teachers to train students in visual science itself, teachers to educate the public about vision.

It is hoped that this book will fill a variety of needs and many pleasurable hours, but most important that it may expand man's understanding of visual science through stimulating the curiosity of future scientists.

JAMES R. GREGG, O.D.

Los Angeles, California
January, 1966

Acknowledgment

For advice and suggestions on experiments and preparation of materials: The Department of Education of the American Optometric Association; Hubert Moshin, of the Rand Corporation; Arthur Heinsen, President of the Vision Conservation Institute. For patiently posing for photographs, Janell and Ronnie and their neighborhood friends. For reference service and indexing, Grace Weiner, Librarian at the Los Angeles College of Optometry. Experiments 2, 6, 17, 28, 29, and 32 are based on material prepared for *Nature and Science Magazine* and are used with permission of the Natural History Press.

Contents

Part I

INTRODUCTION TO THE EXPERIMENTS

Something About Light

You will understand visual science much better if you know what light is and how lenses affect it. Read this section carefully before performing the light experiments.

Light is a form of energy. This means it has the power to do work. It can make objects warm. It can change chemicals into a different form.

In the eye, light affects a chemical in such a way as to release electrical energy. This is called a *nerve impulse*. In the optic nerve, this energy flows from the eye to the brain.

But what is light itself? It is actually a bunch of tiny particles traveling at a tremendous speed. However, the particles of light given off by a source of energy, such as the sun or a light bulb, are not all the same. Some travel a different distance apart; they have a different *wavelength*.

White light travels at a speed of 186,000 miles in 1 second. That is seven and a half times around the earth during the tick of a clock. That is its speed in air. Glass, water, and such substances slow it down. In glass, it moves only 124,000 miles per second.

This slowing-down effect is why glass can bend light. A ray of light that strikes a glass surface at an angle is changed in direction as it enters the glass and its speed reduced. When it leaves the glass, it again changes direction as it speeds up. Diagram 1 (pages 4-5) shows this.

How much the light changes direction in glass depends upon:

1. The angle between the light ray and the lens surface.
2. The density of the glass.

By control of these factors, light direction can be regulated—that is, it can be focused.

Get a magnifying lens and look at it. This is the simplest kind of lens to understand. Both sides of it are curved. The curves make an angle with the light rays that strike its surface. Notice too that the lens is thick in the middle and thin at the edge. This is a *converging* lens. It gathers light rays and brings them together or *converges* them. The lens is said to bring light rays to a *focus*. A converging lens, also called a *convex* lens, makes things look larger.

3

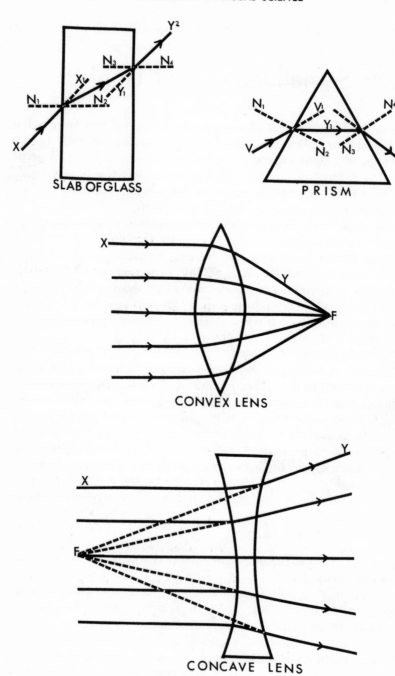

Diagram 1.

A lens that is thin in the middle and thick at the edge is a *diverging* lens. It spreads rays of light farther apart, actually does not bring them to a focus but diverges them. Such a lens is called a *concave* lens and makes things look smaller.

One kind of lens is not really a lens at all. Lenses either converge or diverge light. A prism does neither. A prism only changes the direction of light without converging or diverging it. Yet a prism is sometimes thought of as a lens.

A prism is a wedge of glass. It has flat sides. Light entering its surface at an angle is changed in direction, not focused. Since all wavelengths of light do not travel at the same speed, they are not all bent the same amount. Red is bent least, blue the most. A prism spreads white light into the principle colors. Most lenses do this also in some degree.

That is all the kinds of lenses that there are. Complex optical systems, including the eye, are combinations of these three simple lens forms. Eyeglasses, telescopes, cameras, and optical tracking devices used with missiles all use such lenses.

Lenses are measured in terms of how strong they are—that means

---

Diagram 1. A slab of glass bends light. The entering ray X is bent toward the normal, N1 N2, which is a line perpendicular to the surface of the glass. As it leaves the glass, it again is bent, this time away from the normal, N3 N4. The line X X1 is parallel to line Y1 Y2; thus the ray was deviated but does not change its direction.

The surfaces of the prism work exactly the same as the slab of glass surfaces. The ray V bends toward the normal, the light is slowed down by the glass, thus the bending effect. But as it leaves the prism, the glass surface is at quite a different angle since it is not parallel to the side the ray entered and the bending effect now turns it toward Y2. The light has changed direction.

Each single ray striking the surface of a lens acts exactly the same as the ray shown in the prism. Its direction changes depending upon the angle made by the entering and leaving surface. The difference in lenses is that since their surfaces curve, each individual ray passes through surface points that make a different angle with each other, the result being that each ray is therefore bent a little differently.

Make some drawings like the convex and concave lenses. Apply the principles of ray bending shown in the prism with each individual ray, like X and Y. See if you can in this way understand why converging lenses bring light to a focus; while diverging lenses cause light to spread apart in such a way as to appear to have come from a common point of focus.

how much power they have to bend light, to converge or diverge it. The unit of measurement is the *diopter*. It is a term like a pound, a yard, or a minute. A lens that can bring parallel light rays to a focus 39.37 inches from the lens has a power of one diopter.

Light energy comes from a source such as the sun. The letters on this page do not give off light energy, yet you can see them. How can this be? Few things you see are sources of light energy themselves. The only light sources of importance are the sun and man-made lights. Everything else is seen by reflected light.

Most objects reflect light. Some reflect more light than others. Shiny surfaces reflect a lot of light; dull ones reflect very little. What is reflected depends upon the nature of the surface of the object.

The greater the amount of light a surface reflects, the brighter it appears to be. The volume of light entering your eye also depends upon the surfaces of objects that are reflecting light.

Direction of the light is important too. You can tell where the object is from the direction of the light. Lenses do not change direction of objects seen through them; prisms do.

All your eye has to work with is the amount of light, its wavelength, and the direction the light comes from. Most of the light is bounced off objects, too. From this, your eye gains all the vast knowledge you get from seeing.

Materials and Equipment

What really counts is the principle involved in an experiment, not the equipment. The experiments that follow are designed to be done with as little apparatus as possible. You are expected to use your ingenuity, to make observations that clearly show the function of your visual mechanism rather than devices and gadgets.

Some words of caution are absolutely essential, however. Do not think for a moment that because you can test a function of the eye with a piece of plain cardboard and a pinhole that the function itself is not significant. Your equipment is your eye, and the functions that it performs are truly miraculous.

On the other hand, just because the equipment is generally quite simple, do not think you need not make and use it with the greatest of care. Construct the apparatus as neatly and accurately as you can. Above all, be certain it works as effectively as possible.

There are few instructions and details provided on construction of equipment. Study the illustrations and determine how to make your own. In most cases, there are many ways that it can be done. Remember, what counts is the principle you are testing. If you are preparing a science exhibit, however, make your equipment as attractive as you can, and above all, be sure it works perfectly.

You will need but few things not found around the house. Some experiments require a large magnifying lens. A good light source, flashlight, or a projector is required for several, and to do the ones on color adequately you must have two or three sources. A motor-driven device is helpful for two or three experiments.

Some of the experiments are quite easy, whereas others are much more complex. There is some logic to their order and generally it would be best to work through them. However, few depend upon any previous experiment.

There is no limit to what you might do with some of the experiments. Their purpose is to stimulate your interest and start your experimenting. The rest is up to you. Many will make excellent school science projects, and some are especially good for science fair exhibits. Suggestions are made for further study of certain topics.

Your school science teacher is, of course, a handy advisor. Then, in all probability, your community has an expert on physiological optics, which is the science with which these experiments deals. This expert would be most willing to help. He is your local optometrist.

The optometrist is familiar with all of the phenomena described in this book. He did extensive laboratory experiments on them himself in college. He may have lenses, filters, stereoscopes, and much more that he would be willing to loan to you. He has books for reference that you might not easily find elsewhere. He would be proud to have you ask his advice and counsel.

The Principal Structures of the Eye

Before the astute scientist does an experiment, he becomes thoroughly familiar with the apparatus with which he is going to work in order that he might correctly interpret his results and determine if they are valid or not. In this way also he can avoid errors that might be due to faulty equipment.

The apparatus you are going to experiment with is the human eye. You must be familiar with its parts in order to understand how it works. You will be able to follow the instructions better and enjoy the experiments much more if you study this chapter carefully.

Stand a little to one side and a few inches away from someone's eye. If you have a magnifying lens—a large one used for reading will do nicely—it will help you to observe the visible structures. Look at it for details of the eye's tissues. Remember you are going to do experiments in visual science and you will need to probe deeply into the intricacies of the visual mechanism.

The eyeball itself is slightly egg-shaped and about an inch long. The white part you see is the *sclera*. This is the tough outer layer, which protects the eye and gives it shape. It is like the cover of a ball and serves a similar purpose.

Notice that the front of the eyeball is made up of clear tissue that bulges slightly forward. This is the *cornea*. It joins the sclera, also protects the eye, but is curved a little more than the scleral tissue. Look at the eye from the side to see the cornea best.

The cornea is perfectly transparent so that light can pass through. It acts as a lens, a very strong one, yet it is a living tissue. The cornea provides about seventy-five per cent of the focusing power of the eye. Light rays striking the eye—for example those being reflected from the pages of this book—are *refracted* into the eye by the cornea. "Refracted" means light rays are bent. In the case of the cornea, they are bent, or "converged," into the interior of the eye.

The colored movable curtain behind the cornea is the *iris*. It may be brown, blue, gray, or some mixture of these colors. Study it with as much magnification as you can get. It is actually a delicately beautiful structure made up of many tiny fibers and it often has fascinating color patterns.

The circular opening in the center of the iris is the *pupil*. Actually the pupil is nothing but a hole through which light can enter the eye.

The iris contains bands of muscle that can lengthen and shorten. They are arranged so that when some of the muscle fibers contract, the area of the iris gets smaller. This makes the pupil larger; more light goes into the eye. Other fibers increase the size of the iris area, making the pupil smaller. This serves to cut down the amount of light that can get through.

The iris and pupil make up the light-control mechanism of the eye. It works with remarkable efficiency. It automatically responds as the light changes; it does this from signals sent to it from light-receiving cells inside the eye.

The iris, you can see, is a flat structure, like the diaphragm of a camera. The cornea bulges outward so there is obviously a space between it and the iris. This space is known as the *anterior chamber*. You would not expect it to be empty and it is not. You cannot see it since it is clear, but the anterior chamber is filled with a fluid. This is the *aqueous humor,* which is produced inside the eye itself. If it were not transparent, light could not pass through. Still it serves a function like blood without visible cells. It drains out of the eye through an opening called the *Canal of Schlemm.*

When you look into the pupil, you are actually seeing the lens of the eye, usually called the *crystalline lens.* You cannot actually see the lens in the living eye because it too is transparent. Since little or no light is reflected back out of the eye, the pupil, and in reality the crystalline lens, appears black. The lens is not black; it is a transparent substance. You could see the lens easily if it were removed from the eye.

The crystalline lens is really a lens just as if it were glass or plastic. It provides roughly twenty-five per cent of the total optical power of the eye. But that in itself is not surprising. What is utterly remarkable is the fact that it automatically keeps images sharply focused on the retina, at least as long as it is within its power to do so. Think of that! Suppose you had a camera that focused by itself for any object at which you aimed it. A blurred image on the retina of the eye somehow sets the process in action which causes the lens to change its form, and does so perfectly, at least almost perfectly.

Look at the living eye again, stare deeply into the pupil, and remember you are looking into the crystalline lens of the eye. Now refer to Diagram 2 (page 10). Find the sclera, cornea, anterior chamber, iris, pupil, and lens. Locate these structures in the eye of your subject again. Notice that the diagram shows the eye as though it were cut in half and you were looking down on the lower half of the right eye. Be sure you visualize this properly. Keep the concept in mind as you experiment with this remarkable instrument.

The diagram itself is much larger than a real eye. The crystalline lens, for example, is only about half an inch high and a quarter of an inch thick. The lens is controlled by the *ciliary muscle.* The lens is attached to the ciliary muscle by the *suspensory ligament.* This is a ring of muscle that contracts or relaxes to change the ten-

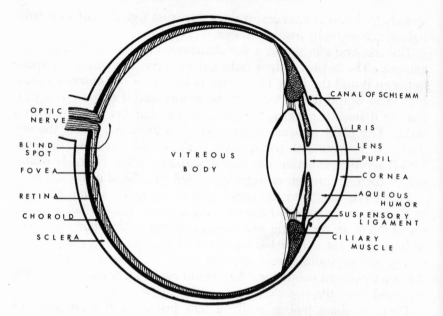

Diagram 2. Horizontal section of a right eyeball. (Courtesy of the American Optometric Association.)

sion on the lens itself. In this manner, though it is by no means simple, the curvatures of the lens surfaces are changed and thus its focusing power is varied. The ciliary muscle can keep incoming light focused all day long. This does not mean it can do this with no difficulty. In fact, in many cases, people must wear lenses when the ciliary muscle does not focus the lens easily.

There is a large space behind the lens, the *vitreous chamber*. It is not empty, nor even full of a water fluid like the aqueous humor. Rather it contains a jelly-like substance—transparent, of course. The material itself is called *vitreous humor*. This vitreous body has an important function; it supports the eyeball. Without it, the eye would collapse like a football with no air. This substance presses against the retina and actually helps to hold that delicate tissue in place.

The *retina* is perhaps the most miraculous structure in the human body. About the size of a postage stamp and the same thickness, it has ten distinct layers, each having a very significant part to play in the retina's functioning. The retina is directly connected to the brain; in fact it is specialized brain tissue placed forward in the skull where light can reach it.

There are about 130 million light-sensitive cells in each retina. Six to ten million of them are called *cones*. They get their name from their somewhat conelike shape. They are responsible for sharp vision and are used primarily in daytime seeing. The cones make color vision possible.

The remaining visual cells, some 120 million, are *rods*. They are generally longer and slimmer than cones. They act differently too. They create no color vision nor can they produce as sharp vision as cones. On the other hand, they are supersensitive to weak light and make it possible for the eye to adapt and see at night.

There is a differential distribution of the rods and cones. Because of this it is not possible to see equally well with all parts of the retina. It is obvious that this is true since you must aim your eye at an object to see it best. This is done so that its image will fall on the *fovea*, a small sensitive spot in the center of the retina giving sharpest vision. It is crammed full of cones and each one has its private nerve fiber to the brain. There are no rods in a tiny central area, only a few nearby.

Be sure to find the fovea in the diagram; it is important to know the fovea's function in order to understand some of the experiments that follow. Supporting tissue, pigment, interconnecting nerve fibers, and a large number of other nerve cells help to squeeze down the information collected by all the rods and cones into only 1 million nerve fibers leaving the eyeball in the *optic nerve*. What a job of organizing must be done!

Actually the eye does not see anything. It sets up signals about incoming light, organizes these signals somewhat, and then ships them to the brain. It is really your brain that does the seeing. But what actually happens when light strikes the retina? How does this finally result in seeing?

Science does not know the full answer to these questions. Still, a lot has already been learned about how the retina works. Light can be thought of as tiny particles of energy traveling at high speed. These pour into the retina like pellets from a shotgun fired into a forest. Some light particles strike the solid molecules of the chemicals in the retinal cells. Some of them miss everything.

Oddly enough, the rods and cones of the retina point away from the light. They stick into tissue that absorbs the light particles missing the visual cells. This is helpful in preventing the light from bouncing around and interfering with image formation.

The rods and cones are something like tiny batteries. When their chemical molecules are hit by a light particle, they give off electrical energy. How much energy is given off depends upon how much light hits active molecules. Light simply releases energy already in the visual chemicals.

If the eye actually worked like a battery, it would eventually run down. This does not happen because there is a recharging mechanism. The chemical balance is upset when light affects it. Energy is necessary, of course. This comes from nourishment that reaches the eye through its network of blood vessels. This takes place primarily through layers of vessels between the retina and the sclera; this is called the *choroid*.

The visual cells in the retina set up nerve impulses, electrochemical changes, which flow into the optic nerve. The *optic nerve* is the trunk line to the brain. Each one contains about 1 million fibers that carry nerve impulses to higher visual centers.

Notice where the optic nerve enters the eyeball. Blood vessels come into the eye through this opening also. This area on the retinal surface is called the *optic disk*. It is slightly oval-shaped, a little longer vertically. It is made up of nerve fibers and blood vessels. There are no visual cells, rods and cones, in the optic disk.

Put your hand at the back of your head just above the top of your neck. You can feel the lower edge of your skull, there is a bump right there. Your hand now covers the major visual areas of your brain. This is where the nerve impulses started in the retina are finally delivered.

The brain is divided in halves. There are two visual areas. The right side of your brain receives what comes from the right side of each eye. The left side of your brain works for the left side of each eye. In some mysterious way, the image halves are fitted perfectly together in perception.

The nerve impulses from the eye are dumped on millions of cells in the brain. Here more electronic-like sorting, classifying, magnifying, and reducing go on. Nerve impulses are sent on to many other parts of the brain. Certain muscles of the body may be made to act because of light falling on the retina. For example, you see a ball—you reach to catch it.

The whole process results in seeing. The chemical and electrical action in the retina, the nerve impulses flowing in the optic nerve and its connections, the action of the visual brain cells all play a part. It is very complex. No one knows for sure exactly how we see because of it.

There is another important fact to remember about your vision. You have two eyes. Not only that, they have muscles that must move them perfectly together. Some of the experiments deal with how well the six delicate muscles of each eye can perform their work.

You have two images, one for each eye. They are blended into a single mental image. This is an involved process that often has surprising results. You will study this too. This process is called *fusion.* Your eyes must work well individually, then their images must be fused together to make human vision what it is—a truly miraculous sense.

Scientists are coming much closer to figuring out the details about how seeing works. Much has been discovered in the last few years. There is still a great deal to learn, however. Perhaps someone reading this book will become a visual scientist and expand the knowledge about vision to the benefit of all mankind.

Suggested Project

Assemble a plastic model of the human eye in order to learn more about its parts. Models and instructions are available at hobby stores in kits ready to be put together and painted. Scientific supply houses also have models, though some are rather expensive and some are already assembled.

Judging Results of Experiments

Only a few of the experiments in this book are *objective* in nature. An objective result is one that you can witness in material objects. Most of the laboratory experiments you have done in school are of this type. The results are in no way related to your own experience, to the reaction of your sense organs.

Most vision experiments are purely *subjective.* They depend upon personal reactions of the individual, not upon material events observed by the experimenter. The results that you, or your subject, get are experiences, or feelings, or perceptions and nothing more. They are related to performance of your body and its own sensory mechanism.

For example, you shine a bright light into the eyes of your subject for a short time. Then, in the dark, he tells you about the colored afterimages he sees. You cannot see his images. The results are purely subjective for him. You can produce afterimages in your own eye, but these are subjective for you.

One very important point then to keep in mind is that *subjective results vary from one person to another.* Not all people interpret things the same way. You must not expect the same results on vision experiments from everyone. You must be very cautious about assuming that there is something faulty with eyes that fail to achieve some of the results. These experiments are not intended to detect faulty eyesight, though in a few instances they may do so.

Normal eyes can perform all of the experiments with no difficulty. The instructions are designed for vision that is operating properly and the results described are based on the same assumption.

Whether eyes are nearsighted, farsighted, or have astigmatism will make very little difference in most cases. Any subject who usually wears glasses for distance seeing should use them in the experiments. Eyes that need a small lens correction but do not have it will perform adequately on most of the experiments.

It is true, therefore, that a person could get good results and still have deficient eyesight. Any person who has doubt about his sight for any reason should have a complete optometric analysis.

None of the experiments will in any manner harm the eyes. It is possible that in some cases they might produce some fatigue or eye-strain if the individual kept at it too long. If anything, the "exercises" of eye muscles and the fusional experiments produce beneficial effects; however, not any of them are designed to suggest cures for deficient sight. It can only be said that certain of the experimental methods are sometimes used to train the eyes to perceive better and faster.

Some of the experiments depend upon the two eyes working together. Undoubtedly some subjects will have difficulty with these, while there may also be some disagreement on the exact results. Particular care must be taken in performing the experiments requiring both eyes to see at once. A little practice may be necessary to eliminate the tendency to see with only one eye. On the other hand, it may require practice to see double when it is expected. Do not be in a hurry to judge results.

Age will be a factor in making the observations that depend upon the focusing ability of the eye. Few people under forty will have any difficulty but above that age, the normal loss of the ability to see close objects will interfere on a few experiments. Keep in mind then that older people are not expected to achieve the same results as younger ones on focusing experiments.

Above all, there is no "wrong" answer possible by any subject. Each individual sees what he sees and that is all there is to it. His response is not wrong for him. True, most people see the same way, but not all are average. The "average" is made up of responses differing from it in both a plus and a minus direction.

You can learn many significant principles by doing vision experiments. In some cases, you should have the subject repeat the experiment several times, perhaps five or ten, then average his answers—for example, when lining up pegs in the depth perception experiment. Some of these techniques will be pointed out as you go along.

Since most of the experiments in visual science are subjective, you must learn to become an expert observer. Follow directions carefully. It will take practice to get the best results. Be sure the experimental conditions are as ideal as you can make them. You must have a very scientific approach to this work.

Watch for even small changes in appearance of targets and images. Report with the greatest accuracy you can. Ask your subject to be careful and to do the same. Remember that the results depend upon *you*, not alone upon objects undergoing change determined by rigid physical laws.

Do you know what the word *stimulus* means? A stimulus is something that arouses a sensory system of the body. In case of the eye, it can be a light or any object that reflects light; in fact it can be anything that results in visual sensation. This term, *stimulus*, will be used frequently in the experiments that follow. You will observe the subjective results of visual stimuli.

Take your time in doing each experiment. Allow your eyes to adjust to viewing conditions. Do not have distractions present, either to sight or hearing. View the objects, whenever you can, against a plain background. Work with the same preciseness that the scientist would use in his research laboratory. Your equipment is one of the most delicate structures known to man—the human eye.

Part II

THE EXPERIMENTS

Experiment 1

REFLECTION OF LIGHT

Apparatus: Cardboard, piece of glass, mirror, ray box

Turn on a flashlight in a darkened room. Particularly if there is a little dust in the air, you can easily see the beam of light emitted by the flashlight. The edge of the beam is a straight line. The width of the beam and how much it increases in width with distance are determined by the reflector behind the bulb.

Hold a black cardboard in the beam. You are not surprised to find the light is cut off by the cardboard. But why is this so? The particles of light energy strike molecules in the paper, or any such solid material, and are stopped. The scientist says light rays are absorbed in this fashion.

Place a piece of glass in front of the flashlight beam. What happens? Why was the light beam not stopped this time? Some of it was. Look around the room and find some light reflected by the piece of glass, where it is depends upon how you tilt it. You can angle it to produce a spot of light on the ceiling, though a much brighter one still images on the wall.

You have shown what reflection is. As shown in Fig. 1–1, some light particles bounce off certain kinds of surfaces and keep on going, some pass through the glass. You have proved, too, that light is something—a tangible—tiny particles that move.

Now hold a mirror in the flashlight beam. Angle it so that there is a spot on the ceiling. Is it brighter than with the piece of glass? Why? How much light is reflected depends upon the nature of the substance. It is important to remember that any shiny, smooth surface reflects some light; this includes lenses and the smooth surfaces of the human eye.

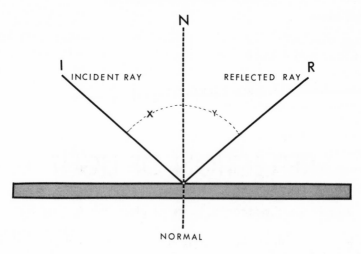

Fig. 1—1. Shows the principle of reflection. The incident ray is turned by the surface so that it makes the same angle with the normal as the reflected ray. Angles X and Y are thus equal. N is perpendicular to the surface.

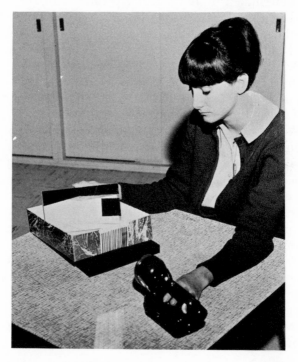

Fig. 1—2. Using the ray box. The slits in the front make ray shadows for demonstrating the principles of reflection.

Exhibit Idea

Cut a window in the end of a box, about 8 inches wide by 12 inches long and 4 inches high. Fasten strips of cardboard over the opening to create a teeth of a comb effect. Light from a source such as a flashlight, a bulb with a reflector, or a beam of sunlight will produce a ray pattern on the bottom of the box as shown in Fig. 1–2.

The ray pattern can be interrupted by a solid, a glass, or a mirror to show the principles of total absorption, partial reflection, or total reflection. At the same time, the angle of incidence and reflection is easily seen by the reflected ray pattern.

How many ways can you think of to use the ray pattern idea? An exhibit board with three sources could be used to show the different principles. Painting the bottom of the box white will produce a sharp ray pattern.

Experiment 2

REFLECTION OF LIGHT BY THE EYE

Apparatus: Cardboard disk, several colored targets, magnifying lens

Have your partner stare straight ahead while you look at his eye from the side. Notice that over the front of the eye there is a bulge of clear tissue, like a curved pane of glass. This is the cornea. It works something like glass. It protects the eye and helps give it shape. But the cornea has another very important job, too. It acts like a powerful lens to bring the image to focus.

Most of the light that falls on the cornea passes through it and enters the inside of the eye. However, some light is reflected. By controlling target size and distance, the power of the cornea as an optical device can be determined. You can get an idea of how this is done by observing images reflected by the cornea.

Make a black and white disk, about 5 inches wide, as shown in the Fig. 2–1. Punch a hole in the center and attach a handle. Now look directly through the hole in the disk at the eye of the subject about 10 inches away. (See Fig. 2–2.) There must be plenty of light falling on the disk. You may need to direct a lamp on it. Look for a small image of the disk reflected in his cornea. It will appear about in the center of his pupil. Move the disk and its image will move.

Hold your finger at the top edge of the disk. Have the subject look at your finger. What is the shape of the reflected disk image now? Try it with your finger on the right side, the left, and the bottom. This shows the cornea does not have a perfectly round and regular curve, but is rather shaped like the end of a football. Observe corneal reflections with targets of different colors and shapes. What do you observe with each?

What you have seen is the cornea working not as a lens, but rather as a mirror. However, it does serve as a lens, forming images

Fig. 2–1. There is a hole in the center for viewing the image of the disk reflected from the cornea.

Fig. 2–2. Observer stands close enough to get a good image of the disk reflected in subject's cornea.

in much the same way as you observed; the images, of course, being formed inside the eye. The cornea provides about seventy-five per cent of the total optical power of the eye.

Observe the reflection from the surface of a magnifying lens in the same way. By holding the lens and target just right, again looking through a center opening, you can see it reflected from the lens surface.

Exhibit Idea

Provide various targets so that observers could see images reflected from the cornea of an eye model. You can also use a series of curved surfaces such as marbles, a magnifying lens, a spectacle lens—in fact, any shiny surface—in order to illustrate reflected images.

Experiment 3

REFRACTION OF LIGHT

Apparatus: Ray box, light source, magnifying lens,
small cardboard screen

Be sure you understand the principle of refraction before you do
this experiment.

Part A

Use the same ray box as in previous experiment. It can be held
in a bright beam of sunlight to produce excellent ray patterns. Notice that the ray shadows of a distant source are parallel to each
other. This is because the sun is at optical infinity.

Hold a large magnifying lens in front of the ray box. (See Fig.
3–1.) You will need to adjust the distance to get a good pattern of
rays. What happens? Why do the rays show this pattern?

Notice that the rays intersect at a point. This is the focal point
of the lens. How far this is from the lens depends upon its power.
You may use a light source (Fig. 3–2), but the rays it produces
will not be absolutely parallel.

Inspect the lens. You can easily see that it is thicker in the middle than on the edges. It is a converging lens. You can see this is
what it did to the rays of light: It refracted them *toward* each other;
it converged them. Why do you think it did so?

If you have lenses of other powers, try them. Perhaps you can
find a diverging lens that will work. Your optometrist may have
some that you could use. They will need to be rather strong lenses.
You may need to make the opening small since most lenses will not
be as large as the magnifying lens.

The magnifying lens—in fact, any converging lens—forms a real
image. Hold the lens near a window and, using a sheet of paper

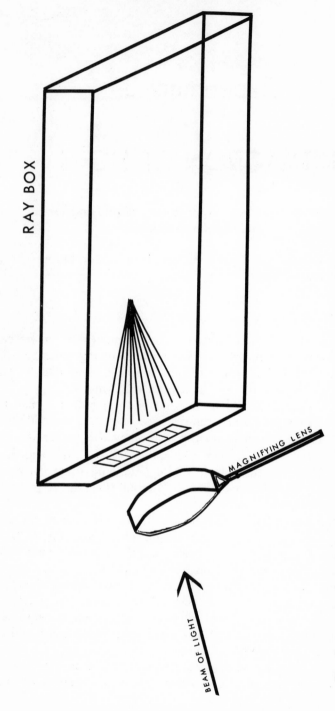

Fig. 3–1. With parallel incident light, the distance from the lens to the point of focus is the focal length of the lens.

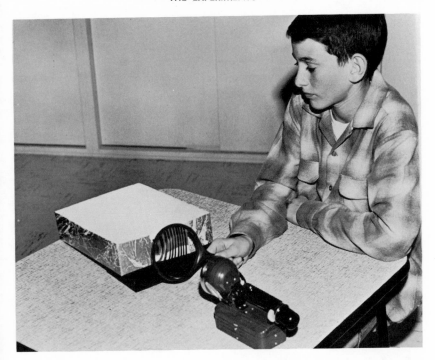

Fig. 3–2. Though not visible here because of the bright photographic light, ray patterns from small sources are easily visible in the bottom of the ray box, especially in a darkened room.

as a focusing screen, produce an image of distant objects on the paper. Is the image upside down? Why is this so?

Part B

Set up a light source, a large lens, and a screen as shown in Fig. 3–3. Cut out a star pattern aperture from cardboard and fasten on front of the light source.

You can manipulate the lens and the light to learn a great deal about focus and refraction. Try various objects. What happens as the object is brought near to the lens? Does the screen have to be moved closer or farther? If you could change the power of the lens, would it have to be stronger or weaker to focus a nearer object on the screen at a fixed distance? What can you learn about images with this setup?

Fig. 3–3. Adjust distance between light, lens, and screen to get a sharp image, in a darkened room.

Exhibit Idea

There are many variations possible. You could make a ray box and use various lenses. Use a prism, which could be cut from plastic, or secure one of glass. You could set up a compound lens system. Experiment and see. The optical bench idea of source, lens, and screen can be adapted in many ways. Use your ingenuity.

Experiment 4

REFRACTION OF LIGHT BY THE EYE

Apparatus: Light source, magnifying lens, cardboard screen,
lens mask

By very careful observation, you can demonstrate how the eye
refracts light just as the magnifying lens refracted light in Experiment 3.

Part A

A slide projector makes an excellent source for several of the experiments in visual science. Set up the lens and screen as in Fig.
4–1. You can, of course, use a flashlight rather than a projector.
Cut a piece of cardboard the size of the magnifying lens. Fasten
it to the lens with tape or hold it against the lens when needed.

Cut two holes in the cardboard—a paper punch will do this nicely
—so that they will both fall within the circular beam of light when
the lens is held in the proper position to focus the light on the
screen. Next adjust the focusing screen forward, without the double-holed cardboard in place, until the image of the projector beam
is well out of focus. When it is in focus, you may get an image of
the bulb of the projector.

Now place the double-holed cardboard up against the lens.
What does this produce on the screen? The two tiny images, produced by the holes in the cardboard, do not overlap because the
object is out of focus. Adjust the screen until the two images of
the holes overlap perfectly.

If you move the screen forward, there are two images—the lens
is not strong enough to focus at the screen distance. It is actually
"farsighted"; the system is not strong enough. A farsighted eye is
not strong enough when its focusing mechanism is relaxed. There
is a big difference, however, between this demonstration and the

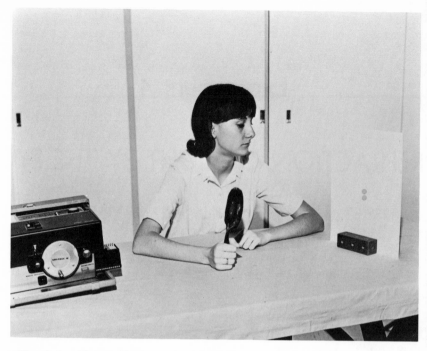

Fig. 4–1. The two holes in the cardboard mounted on the magnifying lens must be closer together than the diameter of the spot of light produced by the projector. Of course, the farther the projector is from the lens, the larger the spot.

human eye. The eye can ordinarily focus on its own to compensate for farsightedness.

Move the screen back beyond the point where the two spots overlap and there is a good focus. Again the images double. The optical system is now too strong, this is like "nearsightedness." The eye, for example, that is "too strong" for the position of its retina is nearsighted.

Remember that this is a demonstration. You can do a similar thing with the eye to demonstrate. The difference is that you will have to control the accommodation of the eye; otherwise it will stay in focus for the object.

Now leave the screen at a fixed distance from the lens. Move the object (the light source) back and forth. If it is too far for good focus, the spots no longer appear single—the system is "nearsightedness." If it is too close, again a doubling of the images occurs. This time the system is "farsighted."

Just as when you moved the screen back and forth, the system is too strong or too weak to focus the object when it is too far or too close to the lens. Now what if object distance and screen position were left fixed and you varied the power of the lens? What can you learn about images and optical systems with this setup? What elements of the eye then might change to make it farsighted or nearsighted?

Part B

Make two pinholes in a stiff black cardboard that is about 2 inches wide. They should be vertical and less than an ⅛ inch apart. Actually they must be separated by less than the diameter of your pupil to work properly. You may need to make several sets of holes to get the distance right. Be sure that the holes have sharp edges.

Draw a horizontal line on white cardboard that can be hung on the wall across the room. View it with one eye through the overlapping area of the pinholes. If your eye is in exact focus for that distance, you will see the line single. It will be double, if you are nearsighted.

The distant horizontal line would also be double if you were farsighted for that point and could let your automatic focusing go—that is, relax your accommodation. It is not likely that you can do this, though some older eyes will show this way that they are farsighted. If you wear glasses, try this without them.

Hold up a pin as shown in Fig. 4–2 while you look at the distant line through the overlapping area of the pinholes. The pinhole will appear double. Why? Is your eye "farsighted" or "nearsighted" for the pin distance?

Look directly at the pin. This will work only for eyes under about the age of forty. The pin will be single, but the distant line will look double. What is the refractive state of your eye with respect to the distant object? Be certain you observe in the overlapping pinhole areas.

There is a way you can test the refractive condition of the eye on a distant object. If it sees it double through the pinholes, it is possible to distinguish whether it is farsighted or nearsighted. Cover one of the pinholes to see which image disappears. See if you can figure it out. Remember, an image seen lowest on the retina appears highest in space. Try it on the lens-object-image set up in Part A to establish the principle.

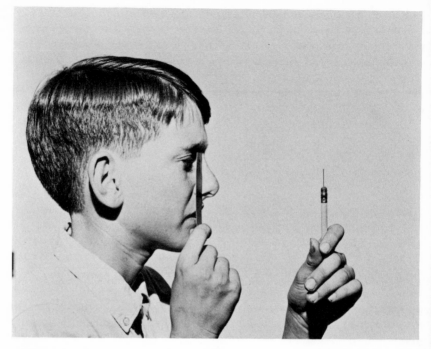

Fig. 4–2. Cardboard with two pinholes must be held very close to the eye; opposite eye is closed.

Exhibit Idea

A double-holed card on a lens would be a very effective way to illustrate optics and apply to the eye. You could demonstrate many image-object relationships. Eye models could be used to show nearsightedness and farsightedness. You could make line drawings to show what you learned from these studies.

Experiment 5

APERTURES AND LIGHT

Apparatus: Light source, object masks, magnifying lens, cardboard screen, apertures

Mount a light source, a magnifying lens, and a screen of cardboard as shown in Fig. 5–1. Paste a black figure on the source to create a dark center image.

Adjust the distance between light, lens, and screen until you get the image on the screen as sharp as possible. Work in a darkened room. Inspect the image carefully. Is it clear to the very edges? Notice the brightness of the image. Can you see details in the inner parts of the image when you substitute a cutout image for a dark one?

Cut some holes in cardboard the size of 50¢, 25¢, 10¢, and one very tiny one. Hold over the lens and inspect the image with each. What are the effects of each size?

This shows that the edges of a lens are not perfect. This is true of most lenses. Of course, the smaller openings cut down light and the tiny opening probably is too small to see sharpening effects; indeed, it may appear to blur the image in some cases.

However, small openings can actually focus light. You can make an image with no lens at all, not a good image, but an image. Take an oatmeal box. Put a piece of tissue paper over the open end, held in place with a rubber band. Punch a hole in the bottom with a large pin.

Hold the pinhole side toward a candle. (See Fig. 5–2.) By adjusting the distance of the box from the candle, you can produce an image on the tissue. Why is it upside down? How is it that an image is produced with no lens at all?

You have observed an important fact in optics. Apertures improve focus. This is true in your eye as well.

Fig. 5–1. The black image on the screen was created here to make it visible. You will not get ones so obvious. Try various patterns on the light source.

If your eye is out of focus, you can improve clearness by a pinhole in a card. Try it. Have your family try. If your parents wear glasses to read, have them try a pinhole for reading without glasses.

You can make cardboard spectacles this way. Put a series of pinholes in cardboard lenses. Wear them outdoors. Hold the magnifying lens close to one eye—everything is blurred; now look through the lens with the multiple pinholes.

Exhibit Idea

For a science exhibit, you could have images focused by several aperture systems. It would be easy to demonstrate to your class, or to an audience; it could be set up so that the observer could test the effects of apertures himself.

Fig. 5–2. View the image of the candle produced by the pinhole camera in a completely dark room.

Experiment 6

APERTURE CHANGES BY THE EYE

Apparatus: Cardboard with small hole, magnifying glass, flashlight

Look at the pupil of your subject's eye in dim light. Notice its size. Stand very close to see it clearly. Now turn on a nearby lamp or shine a light in the other eye. What happens? It may help to use a magnifying glass as in Fig. 6–1.

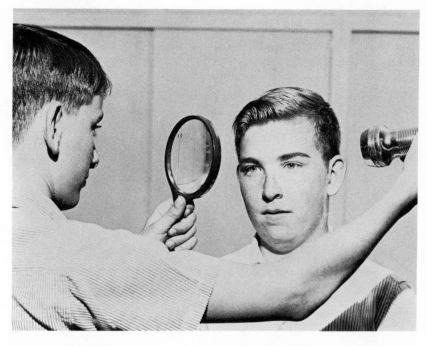

Fig. 6–1. Light directed in one eye causes pupil size to change in opposite eye; this is called the consensual pupil reflex. The change made in the eye receiving the light is called the direct pupil reflex.

Watch the edge of the pupil very carefully to observe its delicate movement. Notice that shining light in one eye causes the pupils of both eyes to constrict. Study the pupillary changes very carefully. Measure pupil size outside in the sun and in a darkened room.

You can even see the effects of your own pupil changing size. Punch a tiny hole 1 inch from the edge in a piece of heavy paper. A thick pin or paper clip will make a hole about the right size. Darken the room but leave space enough at one window to peer out at the sky. Stay in the room a few moments until your eyes get adjusted.

Cover your left eye with your hand as in Fig. 6–2. Look through the tiny hole in the paper at the plain, bright sky with your right

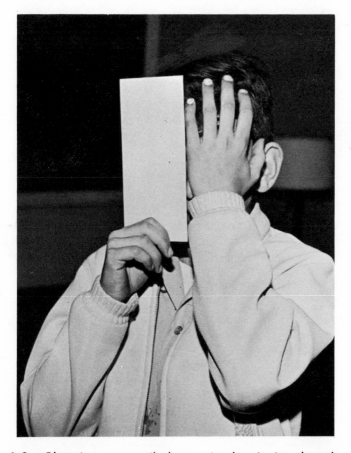

Fig. 6–2. Observing own pupil change size by viewing through a small hole out a bright window.

eye. Hold the hole as close as you can to your eye. Notice carefully how big the hole looks. Now uncover your left eye and watch the hole change size. Does it get smaller, or larger? Cover your eye with the left hand again. What happens to the hole size?

The hole seems to change size because the pupil changes size. This shows that the pupil's job is to control the amount of light that enters the eye.

Make a very tiny triangular hole in the edge of a cardboard. Look through this with one eye. As you move it close to your eye it will look round, proving the circular image you see is your own pupil, not the hole itself.

Exhibit Idea

You could make sketches of the pupil of the eye in different amounts of light. Explain how it works, what it does for vision. Plastic eye models would help to illustrate.

Experiment 7

CHROMATIC DISPERSION

Apparatus: Mirror, flat pan of water

A prism is a wedge-shaped piece of glass. It refracts light—that is, it bends light. (See Diagram 1   pages 4–5.) But not all wavelengths are bent the same amount. The higher speed wavelengths are slowed down more and so are bent more. Thus, a prism will actually spread white light out into the colors of the spectrum.

The edge of a pane of glass, a mirror, or even clear plastic will act as a prism. Or you may be able to obtain a prism from an optometrist. Use the ray box to see how it bends light, but notice that it does not focus.

You can make a satisfactory prism out of water. Place a mirror in a pan with the mirror on the edge of the pan (Fig. 7–1). The water above the mirror is actually prism-shaped. Hold it in a beam of sunlight so that the light passes through the water, strikes the mirror, and is reflected by the mirror onto the ceiling or wall.

What effect is produced by the image? Be sure you understand why. Notice the order of colors in the image on the ceiling. Which color is bent most by the prism? Which least?

Turn the water prism around. Do the colors reverse their position? Is red still on the side of the thin edge of the prism?

This is called chromatic dispersion. You might have noticed this in Experiment 3. Rather than a perfect focus with the magnifying lens, you may have got marked color effects, especially using sunlight as a source. Repeat this and see. In some lenses, there is a great deal of chromatic aberration and you might be able to detect considerable difference in focus of the red and blue, with the other colors in between. Adjust the screen to detect this.

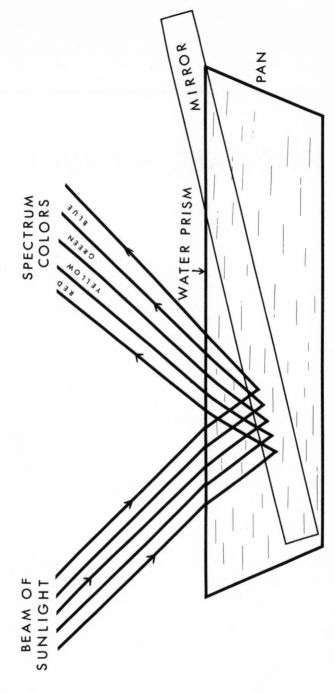

Fig. 7–1. Notice that the layer of water above the mirror forms a prism; it refracts light which is then reflected by the mirror back through the water and into air. This process spreads the white light into the colors of the spectrum somewhat as is illustrated here.

This shows that lenses as well as prisms have chromatic dispersion. How much is dependent upon the type of glass. Most optical systems are designed to prevent this, generally by use of several kinds of glass, in order to keep all wavelengths focusing at a single point.

Exhibit Idea

You could make an exhibit prism showing chromatic effects. It could be done so that one prism spread the wavelengths and another put them back together. You would need to produce a narrow beam of white light.

Experiment 8

CHROMATIC ABERRATION
OF THE EYE

Apparatus: Light source, cardboard square

The human eye, just as the magnifying lens you used in Experiment 3, has chromatic aberration. It will split a beam of white light into colors of the spectrum and you can see it in your own eye.

Cut a narrow, sharp slit in a piece of black cardboard or a sheet of foil to make a mask for your flashlight, a projector beam, or a lamp. Even a small electric bulb can be covered with foil that has a tiny hole in it to make a point source of light.

In a darkened room, look at the tiny light source, whether a slit or a point, with one eye alone. Do you see any color on the edges of the light? Now cover part of your pupil with a straight edge of cardboard as in Fig. 8–1. Move it from the side toward the center of your pupil until you see color effects from the light. What does it look like?

This depends upon a subjective result. Are you a good observer? You may need to look very closely to see the color effect.

Now bring the card in from the opposite side of the same eye. Do the positions of the color reverse with respect to right and left? Why do you think this is so? Remember what you observed in the experiment with the water prism.

Is the optical system of your eye acting like two prisms with their thick sides, their bases, toward each other? Refer again to Diagram 1 to understand why this is so.

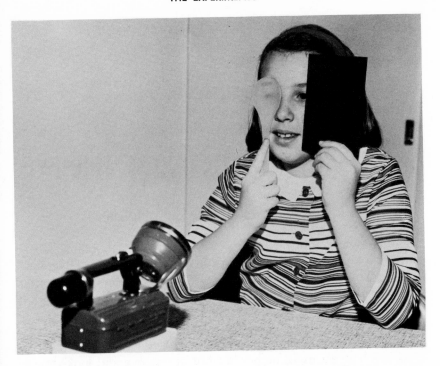

Fig. 8–1. Observing chromatic aberration effects of the eye.

Exhibit Idea

Drawings of the eye and its optical system could depict the chromatic aberration effects of the eye and why they occur. Observers could see their own chromatic aberration by a setup as described above.

Experiment 9

ACCOMMODATION OF THE EYE

Apparatus: Cardboard target with letters

The cornea cannot change its power, but the crystalline lens is controlled by the ciliary muscle inside the eye. Refer to Diagram 1, page 9. The lens automatically bulges the right amount to produce the power necessary to keep vision as clear as possible. This act of focusing by the eye is called *accommodation*.

Make a circle in the center of a piece of paper and put letters around it as shown in Fig. 9–1. Cut out the center of the ring. Hold the hole about 12 inches in front of one eye and look through it at a picture across the room. Are the letters around the hole clear or blurred?

Now look right at the letters on the paper. How does the picture look? This shows that your eye changed focus for each distance. This was done by the lens inside your eye. Try again and be sure.

You are observing one of the most significant functions of the human eye, its *accommodation*. The accommodative ability of the eye slowly lessens; actually this begins about age ten. In the forties, it has dropped to such an extent that it is difficult to focus enough to see near objects. This is why glasses are then necessary for reading and close work.

You can estimate the total focusing power of the eye by measuring how close to your eye you can read a page of small print. Try it on different subjects, one eye at a time. Anyone who wears glasses for distance seeing should have them on when doing this. The older the eye, the less its accommodative power.

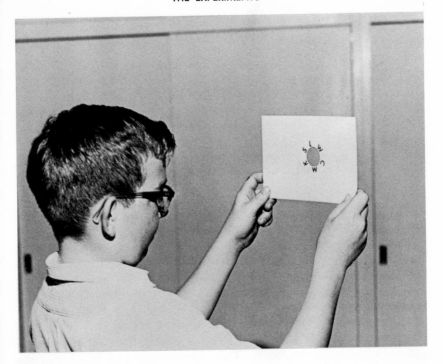

Fig. 9–1. Subject sights through hole at distant object. Letters around opening will appear blurred.

Exhibit Idea

Drawings or models could be made to show the eye's focusing system. Subjects could observe the focus change by looking through an aperture as in this experiment. The limit of accommodative power could be measured on each person.

Experiment 10

INVERTED RETINAL IMAGE

Apparatus: Cardboard square with tiny hole, pin

In Experiment 3, whenever using the magnifying lens, you observed that the image was upside down.

The eye is an optical system in just the same way, so it also has a reversed optical image. Naturally you see right side up. Thus, it might seem that the retinal image is right side up.

The fact is that all images striking the bottom of your retina appear to come from above. This relationship is so natural to you that you have not recognized it.

You also saw this image reversal in the pinhole camera. A lens, such as the lens system in the eye, makes no difference. This can be shown by a pinhole experiment that makes it possible to cast a shadow image on the bottom of the retina without any reversal of its image as normally occurs in optical imagery.

Hold a card with a pinhole in its center about 3 inches from your eye. Move the pin up from below and very close to your eye, touching lashes (Fig. 10–1). Start it slowly until it just comes to the pinhole. Watch carefully for an image or shadow of the pin. Where does it appear to be?

You are seeing a very fundamental principle of visual perception. The shadow of the pin falls on the lower part of your retina. Images on the lower retina are always interpreted as coming from above. It looks that way to you even though you know the pin is really below.

Actually you can prove the principle by simply pushing on the eyeball. Turn your right eye far to the left. Press on the back of the eye. Where does the spot appear to be? Images always appear in space, not on the retina, and where they are in space depends upon the location of the retinal stimulation.

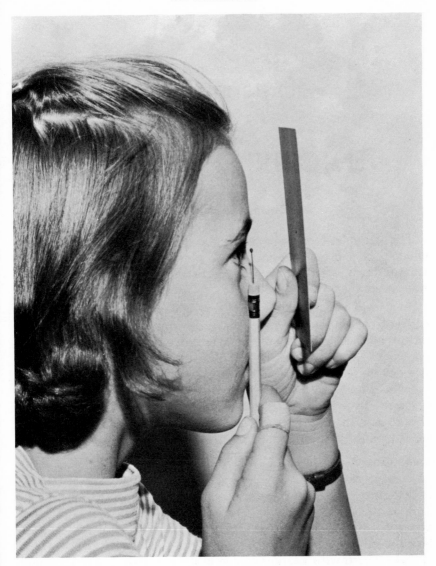

Fig. 10–1.   The pin and card with the hole in it should be held just as shown here in order to get the image reversal effect.

Exhibit Idea

A model of the eye or an optical bench could demonstrate inversion of the retinal image. A lens or optical system would also illustrate this.

Experiment 11

ENTOPTIC PHENOMENA

Apparatus: Card with pinhole

The word "entoptic" means originating within the eyeball. The effects you will see here are due to objects, actually tissue cells of various kinds, which cause shadows to fall on the visual cells in one way or another.

(a) **Cornea.** Look at the sky where it is moderately bright. It is easiest to observe with each eye alone. Notice carefully any irregularities of the uniformity of the field; some of these are due to the cornea and the tear film over it. Droplets of tear fluid on the cornea can be seen as a bright spot surrounded by a dark ring. Blink your eyes and you may see these shadows move.

Exert a little pressure on the cornea by squeezing your lids. Does this change the phenomena? Also press on the cornea through the lids to produce a flattening or wrinkle, and then observe the field.

(b) **Aqueous and Vitreous Chambers.** Objects, actually imperfections of transparency, in the aqueous and vitreous material can be seen as irregular spots floating around in the field. Cover one eye and look at the sky. Do you see any "floaters?" Look down and then straight ahead again quickly. Do any shadows drift and move? Try the other eye.

Take a card with a large pinhole in it (Fig. 11–1). Look through this at the sky. Block one eye; move the pinhole around a bit to cast shadows on the retina. Search carefully for spots and shadows. They may appear like strings of material, or even small circles. Young eyes usually have fewer of these floaters than older ones. Sometimes rather large dark objects appear in some eyes; these are harmless floaters.

(c) **Blood Cells in the Retina.** You can actually see blood cells traveling in your retinal capillaries if you observe very carefully. Again

48

Fig. 11–1. Look out the window at the bright sky through a tiny hole to see entoptic phenomena in your eye.

look at the sky with one eye. Do you see small dancing spots? They appear as bright circles against a dark background. They follow a regular path in the capillaries. They have a movement of their own.

How would you distinguish between the blood cells and objects floating in the aqueous or vitreous? You will need to make careful subjective observations in this experiment. Try different lighting. Experiment until you find the best way to experience floating objects.

Experiment 12

SEEING RETINAL BLOOD VESSELS

Apparatus: Penlight or flashlight

Look at the illustration of the cross-section of the eye (page 10). The blood vessels come in through the opening for the optic nerve. Most of the blood supply lies in the choroid, but some vessels fan out over the surface of the retina. They can actually be seen in the living eye by looking through the pupil into the eye with an ophthalmoscope.

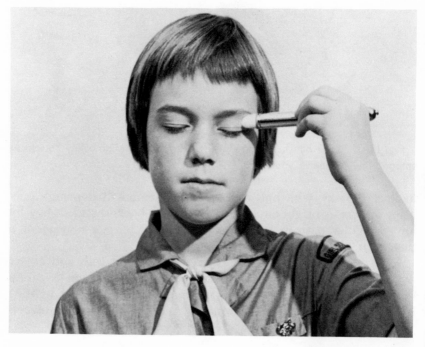

Fig. 12–1. Light directed from the side through the closed lid will cast a shadow of the retinal blood vessels that you can see with careful observation.

Why do you not see the shadow of these blood vessels all of the time? Why is it they do not interfere with seeing? The rods and cones beneath the retinal blood vessels are so constantly shadowed that they get used to it. But when you shine light from the side, the shadow created falls on visual cells that are not accustomed to a shadow.

In a darkened room, shine a tiny beam of light through your closed lid of one eye by holding the penlight on the lid at the side (Fig. 12–1). Move the light slightly. The vessels on the surface of the retina become visible in the field, ahead of you.

Keep the spot of light in motion and shining through the closed lid. The shadows of the larger retinal vessels will appear as branching treelike figures. Follow these "downstream" and obtain a view of the optic disk where the vessels enter the eye. Look at Fig. 12–2, which shows the pattern of retinal vessels.

Exhibit Idea

Models and sketches can be used to show the retinal circulation.

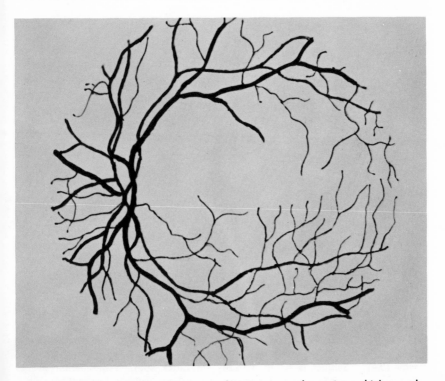

Fig. 12–2. The pattern of veins and arteries on the retina which can be seen as a shadow when the eye is lighted from the side through the closed lid.

Experiment 13

FIELDS OF VISION

Apparatus: Fixation object, wand with test object

Close one eye. Look steadily at a point on a distant wall with the other eye. Notice how much space you can see without moving your eye. This area, the visible area, is called your *visual field.* Try it with the other eye. Can you see the same area? How much more space can you see with both eyes than with either eye

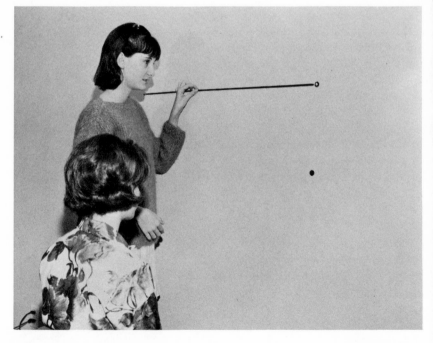

Fig. 13–1. Subject is fixing steadily on black spot. Experimenter moves white dot on wand from out of subject's visual field until it is just visible.

alone? Do you think this is much of an advantage—that is, having a two-eyed field rather than a one-eyed field?

Roll up a piece of paper into a tube. Look through it at the spot on the wall. How much space do you see now? You can still see the object point clearly but imagine what it would be like to have tunnel vision. Try to walk around looking through the tube. What value do the fields of vision have?

When looking straight ahead, with each eye alone you should be able to see about 90 degrees to the right and left, about 90 degrees downward, and about 70 degrees upward. Side vision is not sharp vision, but it is sensitive to the presence of objects and the size of the visual field is important to seeing properly. Diseases of some kinds, fatigue, certain drugs, and tobacco can reduce the size of the visual field.

Make a wand of wood or wire. Attach a white spot about ¼ inch in diameter on the end. Test a subject's visual field by having him sit about 3 feet from a plain wall (Fig. 13–1). Place a small fixation object on the wall at the subject's eye level. While he looks steadily at the fixation object with one eye, move the wand object in from outside of his visible field until he reports he first sees it. Repeat at about 15-degree intervals to determine the outer limits of his field at a sufficient number of points to plot it accurately.

Be careful, however, in judging any result you get. Your field-plotting is only for illustration and not reliable for diagnosis.

Exhibit Idea

Display charts and plots of visual fields for normal eyes, showing how much larger the field is with two eyes. This could be related to a model of the eye. Include some of the advantages of two eyes. In a participation exhibit, visual fields could be plotted.

Experiment 14

THE RETINAL BLIND SPOT

Apparatus: Small wire wand and test spot, black sheet of paper, chalk

There are no rods and cones where the optic nerve enters the eye. Look at Diagram 1. Notice that the optic disk is an oval area of considerable size, actually about 6 by 8 degrees. Your eye is actually blind in this area.

Make a wand with wire. Attach a small white spot about ⅛ of an inch in diameter. Mark a fixation spot in the center of a black sheet of paper at least 8 by 10 inches in size.

Have a subject sit about 12 to 15 inches from the black paper, which is mounted on the wall at eye level (Fig. 14–1). While the subject covers one eye and looks steadily at the fixation spot, move the spot on the wand around until the subject says that it disappears. This will happen when it is placed so that its image falls on the optic disk of his open eye.

Now move the spot until it reappears. Do this in various directions, marking the point of reappearance on the sheet with chalk. The subject, of course, must not move his eye but must continue to look at the fixation mark. In this manner, you can plot out the exact size and shape of his blind spot. How large do you find it to be?

Make an estimate of the width of the blind spot in your field a hundred yards from your eye. Would it be big enough for a whole automobile to disappear in it? Why do you think you cannot actually recognize your blind spot by simply closing one eye and trying to locate it? Why does not the presence of this blind spot handicap you in seeing?

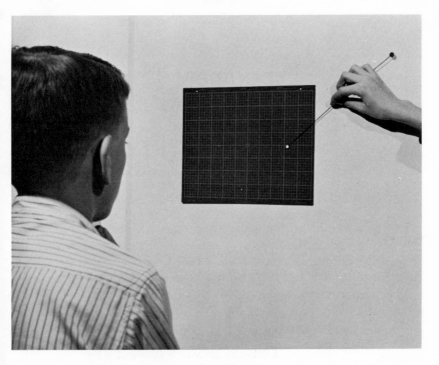

Fig. 14–1. The white target is in the blind spot of the subject's right eye as he fixates the very center of the black rectangle.

Exhibit Idea

Make a sketch of the retina and its blind spot. Trace the optic nerve back to the brain. Demonstrate how the blind spot can be plotted for subjects who view the exhibit.

Experiment 15

VISUAL ACUITY

Apparatus: Appropriate black letters on white disk

The term *visual acuity* generally means the sharpness of vision —that is, how well the eye can see fine details. However, this is a broad subject and you must realize that this experiment only illustrates visual acuity and it by no means covers its many facets.

The most common measure of visual acuity is the Snellen fraction:

$$\text{Visual acuity} = \frac{\text{Distance at which test is made}}{\text{Distance at which smallest letter}}$$
read subtends an angle of 5 minutes.
(One minute is $\frac{1}{60}$ of a degree.)

For your purposes here, you need not concern yourself with why the letters are constructed to make an angle of 5 minutes. But you should understand that visual acuity is a measure of seeing the smallest letters possible, and that is, of course, directly related to the angle subtended by these letters at the eye of the observer. The basic problem then is measuring the size of the angle created by letters that are just readable.

Therefore, you can measure visual acuity by using a letter of fixed size and changing the viewing distance. This is the same as maintaining a fixed test distance and changing letter size. In either case, a fraction is used to express the size of the angle that the just readable letters represent.

Cut the three letter E's from black paper exactly the same size as those in Fig. 15–1. Mount each on a white cardboard background about 12 inches in diameter, refer to Fig. 15–2. Fix a handle on the back so you can hold the card from behind. The smaller E subtends an angle of 5 minutes at 20 feet, the middle one does so at 50 feet, and the large one makes a 5-minute angle at 100 feet.

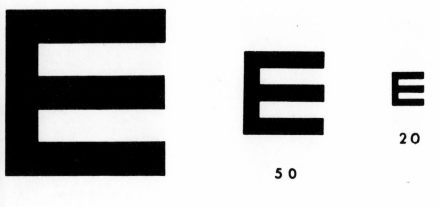

Fig. 15–1. Exact size of letters that subtend an angle of 5 minutes at the distance indicated in feet.

Have your subject stand more than 20 feet away while you hold the small E with its open side in some direction unknown to the subject. Make the test with each eye alone and both together. Have the subject move slowly forward until he can correctly indicate with three fingers the direction of the open side of the letter.

Measure the distance in feet from the target to the point at which the subject correctly orients the small E. Divide this value into 400. The quotient becomes the denominator of the Snellen fraction; the numerator is 20. For example, if the subject must move to 10 feet to see the E properly, $400 \div 10 = 40$. Thus his visual acuity is 20/40.

If the subject cannot see 20/20 E when he reaches 10 feet from the target, use the 20/50 and start him again at 20 feet. To calculate the common Snellen fraction, divide the distance at which he can orient the middle-sized E into 1000. The figure 20 over this quotient will be the visual acuity rating. Example: Subject moves to 5 feet from target before he can detect open side of the 20/50 E; $1000 \div 5 = 200$. Thus, his visual acuity is 20/200.

You will get figures that do not always come out even; in such case round them off to the nearest multiple of ten if they are under 100, to a multiple of 20 between 100 and 200, or to multiples of 50 over 200. Testing should be done with and without glasses for each subject.

Should an even larger letter be necessary to get a valid measure-

Fig. 15–2. Subject moves forward until he can just detect the open side of the letter E.

ment, use the 20/100 E. Copy its size exactly. It must be of a dull contrasty black on a white background. A separate target holder is necessary for each letter. With the large E, the dividend number is 2000.

Do not try to judge the cause or consequences of any subject's visual acuity that is poorer than the standard 20/20. If there is significant blur of either eye, he should find out what causes it and whether it should be corrected, if he does not already know. This should be done by an optometric examination. But that is not the purpose of this experiment; it is only to demonstrate what visual acuity is and how it is measured.

It has already been pointed out (page 11) that only the very center of the retina has sharp visual acuity—this is produced by images falling in the fovea. You can observe this very easily with the E device. Have the subject fixate your finger held at the very edge of the cardboard background of the large E. Have him move forward until he sees the E correctly; then calculate his visual acuity.

Measure the acuity of side vision even farther from the fovea by holding a pencil for the subject to fixate at varying distances from the letter E. Why does this show the sharpness of side vision? Why is it that everything in your field of view seems clear to you when it really is not?

It is equally important that you do not misinterpret the meaning of sharp vision, 20/20 acuity. It is but one small part of seeing comfortably and efficiently. The experiments in this book deal with many more skills and functions of the visual mechanism. Side vision, muscle control, dark adaptation, focusing ability, and many more are essential to good vision. None of these is measured by visual acuity. Thus 20/20 acuity by no means proves that a person has "perfect sight."

Exhibit Idea

Prepare diagrams showing what visual acuity is, including sketches of the retina pointing out where vision is sharpest. Demonstrate methods of testing visual acuity. Explain various factors that would reduce visual acuity.

Experiment 16

DARK ADAPTATION

Apparatus: Black cardboard square, small white circle and square

When you go from the bright outdoors into a dark room, you are nearly blind at first. Soon you can see quite well in the dim light; you could walk around without bumping into things. Your eye has gone through a process of *dark adaptation*. The retina becomes more sensitive because a chemical called *rhodopsin* automatically increases its concentration in the dark.

It is known that rhodopsin is found in the rods. It changes rapidly in the first 5 minutes in low illumination, but dark adaptation continues slowly for an hour. This remarkable chemical can increase the sensitivity of the eye a million-fold. Under perfect conditions, a completely dark-adapted eye can see the light of a candle 14 miles away.

You can watch the dark adaptation process work by going from a lighted room to a dark one in your house at night. See how long it will take you to see the numbers on a clock with a luminous face. Or see how long it takes you to see to read in the room if there is some dim light from a window or open door.

You can see a dim light better by not looking directly at it. This is because there are no rod cells in the center of the retina. To get an image on the rods it must fall off the retinal center. A very weak star in the heavens will appear brighter if you look a little to one side of it. Try this some night.

On a black cardboard about 8 inches by 10 inches in size, paste a white spot about 1 inch in diameter. Paste a 1-inch white square so that there is a 2-inch space between their edges. Hold this as you would a book to read. (See Fig. 16–1.) You need to do this at night in a room where you can darken it so that there is very little light.

Have someone suddenly darken the room. When your eyes have

Fig. 16–1. Subject watches white spots appear in room suddenly changed from very bright to almost darkness.

dark adapted enough, you will begin to see the spots on the black cardboard. Notice that the circle is seen better if you do not look directly at it but aim at the square instead. Now look at the square. What happens to the circle? Can you explain why this is so?

Read again what it says about there being no rods in the center of the retina. Does the experiment prove this? Does it prove that dark adaptation is a function of the rods?

Exhibit Idea

Make sketches of the retina to show its rod and cone population. Relate this diagrammatically to dark adaptation. List the principal functions of the rods and the cones.

Experiment 17

FLIGHT OF COLORS

Apparatus: Flashlight with cardboard mask

When light strikes your eye, it is brought to a rough focus by the cornea, the pupil adjusts the amount of light, the lens produces sharp focus; but it is up to the *retina* to start the process that will result in seeing. You can get some idea of the action of the retina's electrochemical system in this experiment.

Cut a heavy cardboard to the size of your flashlight lens. Make a small hole in the center and fasten the cardboard to the front of the flashlight. Be sure it wi'l produce a tiny but very bright beam of light. Do the experiment in a completely dark room. Wait for 5 to 10 minutes to give your eyes a chance to dark-adapt.

Hold one eye shut, and with the spot of light only an inch or two from your eye, look at it steadily while you count to forty very slowly. (See Fig. 17–1.) Turn the light off, close your eyes, and hold your hand over them to make it as dark as possible. Wait a few seconds, then look for an image of the bright light. A spot will finally appear. Watch it as long as it lasts. This may be several minutes.

This is called an *afterimage*. Does it change color? Be patient, repeat until you have success. Look at the brightest part of the light through the hole. How many colors are produced? Increase the exposure time to a minute or more if necessary to get a good result.

The retina started the activity that resulted in a visual sensation you saw as a prolonged afterimage. But the whole process is very complex. Nerve impulses traveled from the retina to the brain where seeing actually takes place. It would be very interesting for you to speculate as to why you see first one color, then another.

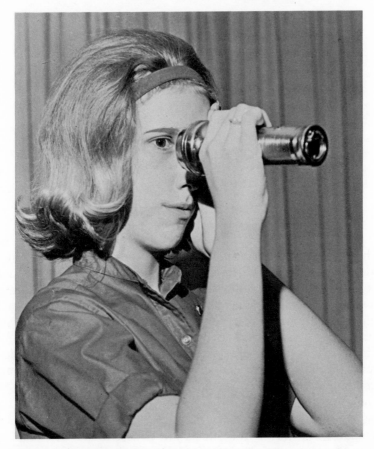

Fig. 17–1. Steady fixation of a tiny spot of light created by a hole punched in a cardboard covering the flashlight produces a "flight of colors" then seen in absolute darkness.

Exhibit Idea

Make a further study of the retinal chemicals. Diagram some of these chemical reactions and illustrate how the eye reacts to light.

Experiment 18

AFTERIMAGES

Apparatus: Cardboard and paper of a variety of colors, uniform gray surface on which to view images

There are a limitless number of visual afterimages that you can produce. The term *afterimage* means, of course, that the image lingers on after the stimulus that created it has ceased. It is called a *positive* afterimage when it contains the light and shade of the original sensation. It is a *negative* afterimage if the image is the reverse in light and shade of the original.

The most interesting ones are *induced* afterimages. The induced effect is produced by a secondary stimulus. This may be a complex target pattern, or a uniform field of gray or of some color. First the eye is stimulated for a short time with a pattern, a form, or a color; then it looks at a dim gray surface, or any other object for that matter. However, the effects are easiest to see if a plain secondary stimulus is used.

Figure 18–1 illustrates some objects that can be used to produce afterimages. Block off the rest and fixate one figure for 20 to 30 seconds; even a full minute is not too long. Then look at a gray paper. It works best if the room is rather dim. You can project an afterimage of the bird and see it flying on the ceiling or in the palm of your hand.

Cut targets from various colors of paper, make up your own shapes. When you look at a gray surface, the afterimage will appear in the complementary color of the original. This is the basic principle involved in induced afterimages.

The first stimulus tends to use up the electrochemical energy of the visual system for that particular stimulus and increase the sensitivity of the eye to the opposite. A red target, for example, uses up the "red energy" and the eye becomes more sensitive to "green," the complement of red (actually a blue-green). This simple statement would not satisfy the visual scientist, but it will do for your purpose here.

Fig. 18–1. Targets like these can be mounted on gray cardboard. To produce the greatest effect, plenty of light is needed on the objects; then subject sees afterimage on neighboring gray area.

Fixate the letter G with your right eye, blocking the left with the palm of your hand. Look steadily for 1 minute, then notice the afterimage. Now block your right eye and see if the afterimage of the G is visible with your left eye? What does this show about induced afterimages?

Gray paper is actually white of low brightness. White contains all wavelengths. Thus, when red is the first stimulus and then you look at gray, green appears in the induced afterimage; the green wavelengths coming from the gray paper seem brighter because the retinal chemicals relatively have increased sensitivity to green.

Now suppose the second stimulus were the same color as the first. Try it. Use a bright red square for the first stimulus, look at it for a minute. Then look at a plain paper of the same red color rather than gray. What is the appearance of the induced image?

Repeat as above, but this time use a blue-green, the complement of the original red, as the secondary stimulus. How does the induced image differ from what was seen with gray? Try mixing various colors. Use a variety of primary and secondary colors.

Exhibit Idea

The pattern of concentric circles as in Fig. 18–2 is a very powerful stimulus to produce an afterimage. It would make a striking example for a display. Make a large ring pattern, 12 or 18 inches in diameter. Provide a gray surface for a secondary stimulus. In color, it is particularly potent.

Your exhibit could incorporate all of the combinations described in this experiment. Design patterns of greatest interest to an audience. Large targets could be made for class demonstrations.

Make a flag pattern with the stripes green and a star field of yellow. Its afterimage viewed against a dark background will appear in the proper colors of the American flag. Can you make other designs that would produce such startling effects?

Fig. 18–2. Motion and rolling effects, as well as a strong afterimage, are produced by a large target like this.

Experiment 19

PERSISTENCE OF VISION

**Apparatus: Sketch of a bird and a cage, colored
slide projector, yardstick**

Moving pictures of course do not move. Neither do television
pictures. Both are simply a series of still pictures, each successive
one following the other so quickly that the eye cannot detect the
interval between them. This is possible because of the persistence
of vision. Movement itself, however, is due to still another phenomena, which is covered in Experiment 35.

Each visual sensation lasts longer than the stimulus that created
it. This persistence makes one image blend into the next so that
it is actually possible to see two images at once under certain viewing conditions.

Figure 19–1 shows a thaumotrope. This is the name given to a
device that can be twirled to demonstrate the persistence of vision.
The figure on one side produces a visual image that persists long
enough to appear to blend with the figure on the other side.

Make a bird and cage on each side of a cardboard square as
shown in Fig. 19–2. Push a pin down through the cardboard edge
to mount it on the end of a pencil. When the target is twirled, the
bird will appear in the cage.

You can perform a rather startling demonstration of the persistence of vision if you have a colored slide projector (a movie
projector would work also). Hold a sheet of paper, notebook size,
a few feet in front of the projector. You do not need the projector
screen; in fact it is better if you do not aim the projector at a wall or
anyplace where it can produce a good image. Put a slide in the
projector and focus it on the paper to give an image about the size
of the paper.

Cover one side of a yardstick with white paper for 10 or 12 inches
on the end. Hold the yardstick at one end so that it is horizontal.
Position the white-papered end exactly where you held the sheet of

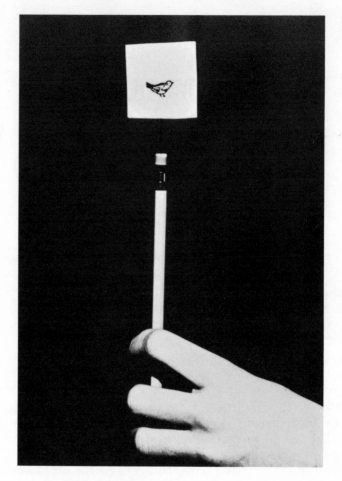

Fig. 19–1. A thaumotrope.

paper to focus the slide. You can move the yardstick in or out to get the small strip of slide imaged on it in good focus. Now move the yardstick briskly up and down.

You will see the entire image of the colored slide floating in air where you are moving the yardstick. It is easiest to view if someone else moves the yardstick while you stand back beside the projector. The whole picture is visible because the top of the picture imaged on the stick, when it is at the top, persists all the time the stick is imaging the rest of the picture all the way down to the bottom line of the picture.

Did you know that this is similar to the way a television picture

Fig. 19–2. The two sides of a target used to illustrate the persistence of vision.

is produced? An electronic beam sweeps along to produce horizontal lines of the picture. The eye still sees the top line while the bottom one is being produced. This, of course, is due to the persistence of vision.

Exhibit Idea

There are many ways you could produce a thaumotrope; any method to make the two-sided target spin rapidly would do. Design some unique targets. A movement device could demonstrate persistence of vision as you did with a yardstick. Tie this in with making television possible.

Experiment 20

SIMULTANEOUS
CONTRAST EFFECTS

Apparatus: Cardboard, water paints, two light sources,
colored filters

The last four experiments have all dealt with the electrochemical,
the physiological processes of the visual mechanism. They have
shown that light energy starts action in the retina, which continues
after the stimulus itself is no longer present. Thus, one stimulus
can have an influence on the sensation created by a stimulus that
follows. But the influence of one stimulus upon another is not only
in the dimension of time; it can happen simultaneously.

This means that what takes place in one part of the retina can
have an influence on what sensations are produced by another part.
The simplest illustration of this simultaneous contrast follows.

Cut three gray squares from the same piece of paper. (See Fig.
20–1.) Place the squares on different backgrounds of white, gray,
and black. Do the squares all look the same grayness?

Simultaneous contrast occurs. Brightness—the white, for example—tends to induce darkness in the area next to it. Black does the
opposite. This amazing process tends to enhance contrast, actually
makes vision better to some extent.

When you look at Fig. 20–2, you will see gray spots at the junction of the white lines. At least, there is a gray spot until you try
to look directly at it. When you aim your eye at a line junction,
its image falls in the rod-free area of the retina and contrast is en-
hanced. Elsewhere, the junctions stimulate the retina where there
are many rods and here the black areas tend to spill over into the
junctions. This is generally classified as a brightness contrast illusion and not actually explainable.

Fig. 20–1. The gray squares are cut from the same piece of paper, yet look different because of background contrast.

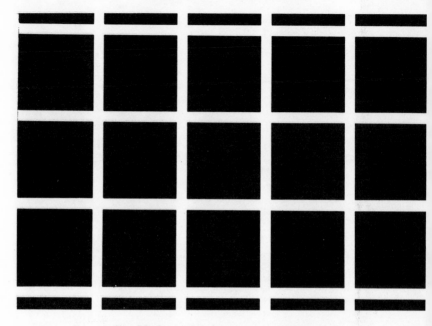

Fig. 20–2. A brightness contrast illusion.

Color effects can also be induced. Try simultaneous color contrasts by placing colored squares cut from the same paper on various backgrounds, gray as well as colors that are similar and complementary to the square.

Color contrasts can be produced most effectively by cutting a small square, ½ inch to 1 inch across, in the center of a large colored square. Then place a gray paper behind the open square. The large field of color will readily produce its complimentary color on the small gray area.

Exhibit Ideas

(a) Use two colored slide projectors. Cut a small ¼-inch hole in thin metal or black plastic that can be mounted as a slide. Make two of these, which are to be used to project a spot of light on a nearby screen. These can be used to produce colored shadow effects.

Place a color filter in front of the lens of one projector; a piece of colored cellophane will do—perhaps several layers to get enough density (Fig. 20–3). Glass filters, Wratten gelatin filters, or plastic

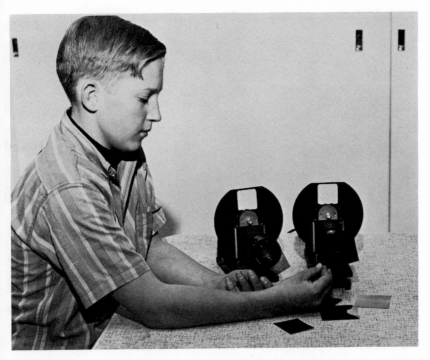

Fig. 20–3. A colored filter over only one projector will induce its complement in the adjacent spot produced by the other projector.

colors can be used. Adjust the other projector so that the projected
spots partly overlap. If green cellophane is used, a pink color will
be produced in the spot of the white projector not overlapped by
the green spot. You may need to reduce the brightness of the white
spot by holding some tissue in front of the projector. For an effective exhibit, it would be best to have a rheostat control for the
projectors.

Various color filters can be used to produce different effects. By
holding a stick in front of the projector with the color filter, the
stick will block out the color. The shadow of the stick will be filled
in with light from the white projector and it will take on the induced
color. You can produce amazing effects using various colors.

(b) An extremely dramatic demonstration of induced color can
be made with the device shown in Figs. 20–4 and 20–5. You could
be sure of interest and attention to your exhibit with this induced
color phenomena. The description of the device is given with the
figures. You may want to experiment with other colors than those
shown. Try other sizes as well.

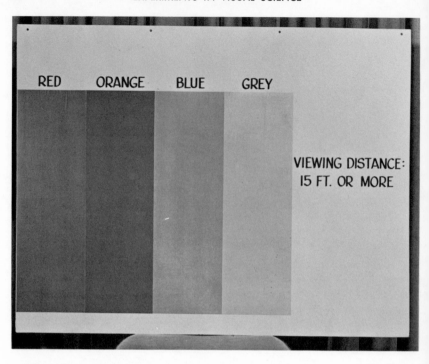

Fig. 20–4. This is a large cardboard, 30 by 40 inches. The strips of color are very bright show-card color paints. Its purpose is to provide the color that appears through the open squares of the cardboard shown in Fig. 20–5.

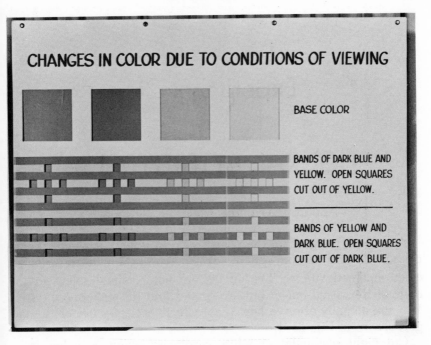

CHANGES IN COLOR DUE TO CONDITIONS OF VIEWING

BASE COLOR

BANDS OF DARK BLUE AND YELLOW. OPEN SQUARES CUT OUT OF YELLOW.

BANDS OF YELLOW AND DARK BLUE. OPEN SQUARES CUT OUT OF DARK BLUE.

Fig. 20–5. This 30- by 40-inch cardboard is attached at the top over the one in Fig. 20–4 so that it can be raised up to illustrate what is beneath. Notice on the board itself how the open squares, ¾ inch square, are cut from yellow bands above, dark blue below.

The panel is positioned vertically while the subject views it from about 15 feet. He notes the color in each of the open squares. All those with the red color strip underneath will appear the same red color. The other color strips will also look the same all the way down the panel. The subject must first make sure that it is the same color up and down.

The panel is then tilted backward until it is nearly flat—try to see exactly how much tilt is needed. The subject now compares the color in the open squares. The results are very dramatic if the device is constructed exactly as shown. It is, of course, a phenomenon of simultaneous color contrast.

Experiment 21

FIGURAL AFTEREFFECTS

Apparatus: Figures drawn on cardboard

An object, imaging on the retina, sets up a field of electrochemical activity in the visual system. It is much like a field set up by an electromagnetic force. The effects are not confined solely to the edge of the visual image but are spread into the surrounding area. You can actually observe how these effects occur by use of the targets shown in Fig. 21-1.

Cut eight rectangles of white cardboard about 3 inches by 6 inches. On each, mark a small X in the center to be used as a fixation point. Construct the figures shown on each of the rectangles A, B, C, D, E, F, G, and H. They can be made with India ink or with black tape. Narrow craft tape of various widths can be purchased at art supply stores.

Most line drawings of the illustrations in this book were first produced with craft tape, including Fig. 21-1 itself.

Place card B behind card A. View A as shown in Fig. 21-2, staring steadily at the small fixation X for 2 minutes. Sit about two feet from the cards. Then remove card A and look at B as in Fig. 21-3. Still fixing on the X, notice the difference in appearance between the right and left rectangle. How does the "old" figure, the right-hand rectangle, compare with the new one?

The theory is that the "old" figure looks dimmer, smaller, farther away because the retinal energy that it released flows out into a field, the area around the exact image itself. You can test this idea by using the other set of cards. They will prove that aftereffects are not confined exactly to the edge of the image.

Use cards C and D in the same manner as A and B. Note the effect on the right-hand square in D, after observing C, even though

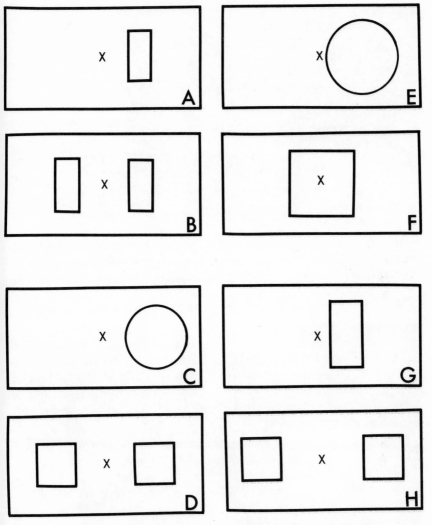

Fig. 21–1. Targets to be used to produce figural aftereffects.

the square does not touch the circle, but falls only in the "field" of the circle.

The field effect is greater inside the limits of a circle than outside. This would follow the principles of an electromagnetic field. E and F will prove this. After the 2-minute inspection of E, the right side of the square on F will appear dimmer, smaller, perhaps pointed away. If you do not easily get results on any of the cards, use an

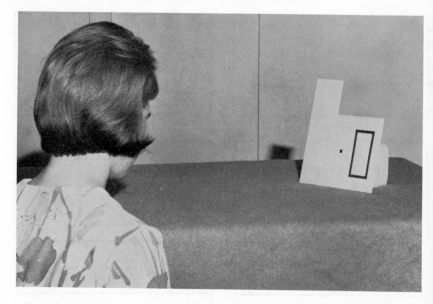

Fig. 21–2. Steady fixation of the X for a 2-minute inspection period.

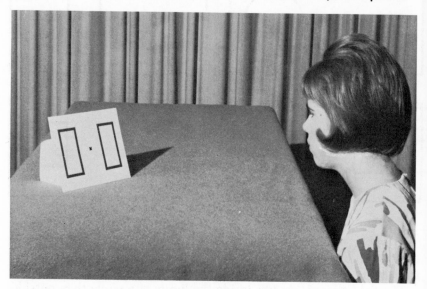

Fig. 21–3. Comparison of appearance of right and left rectangles after previous exposure of right side only for 2 minutes.

inspection period of more than 2 minutes.

In view of what you have seen with the other demonstrations, predict what will happen with cards G and H before you try it. What does this show about field theory?

There are many other patterns that can be used to test and demonstrate figural aftereffects. Construct some of your own.

Exhibit Idea

Large figures such as described in this experiment could be used to demonstrate to individual subjects. These would require the experimenter to be in attendance at the exhibit. Diagrams could illustrate figural aftereffects.

Experiment 22

EYE MOVEMENTS

Apparatus: Penlight, fixation objects, mirror

The fovea is an area of the retina that produces sharpest vision. Refer to Diagram 2 on page 10. If you want to see an object clearly, you must move your eye so that its image will fall in the fovea. It takes the combined action of the six muscles that attach to the eyeball to make the proper movements.

Fig. 22–1. Watch the subject's eyes as they follow a moving object.

Not all eyes can move with equal accuracy and efficiency. You can observe and test this with some careful studies of eyes in motion. The results are purely objective. It will be up to you to watch your subjects' eye movements and to judge how well they perform.

(a) **Pursuit Movements.** Following a moving object is called a *pursuit eye movement*. The ocular muscles must move the eye in such a way as to keep the image in the fovea. Use a penlight or the end of a pencil as a fixation point. As in Fig. 22–1, have the subject follow the object as you move it slowly in a circle. Reverse direction; also move in other patterns such as a figure eight.

Do the eyes follow perfectly? Do they jump along? Cut corners? Overshoot? Try each eye alone as well as both together. You would expect eyes to follow with reasonable accuracy.

(b) **Jump Fixational Movements.** Looking from one fixed object to another is called a *jump fixation*. This is a different kind of eye movement from a pursuit movement. The eye must locate the second object with side vision; then muscles must move the eye in the right direction and the right amount to get its image in the fovea.

Make two fixation targets such as a small square and circle cut from paper. Have your subject seated in front of you so that you

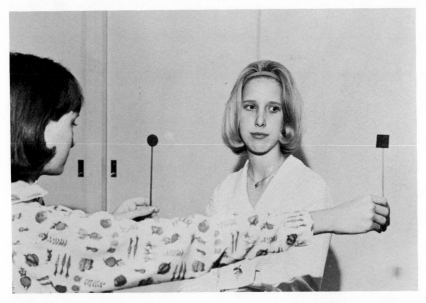

Fig. 22–2. Subject looks from one object to another on command of observer.

can watch eye movements as you give commands to fixate one and the other. (See Fig. 22–2.) Are the movements smooth and regular? Does the eye stop exactly on the fixation point? Try each eye alone. Repeat with fixation targets different distances apart and in different directions.

Ask the subject whether he thinks he is making accurate movements. Try it with other subjects. You will find that the person is unaware of inaccuracies of his fixation.

(c) **Eye Movements and Reading.** Reading is done with a series of jump fixations; the eye does not move smoothly along a line of print. The fewer fixations made per line, the greater the reading speed, provided comprehension is adequate.

Fig. 22–3. Mirror is held to observe subject's eye movements while reading.

Position yourself and a subject as shown in Fig. 22–3. Hold the mirror so that you can see the subject's eyes as he reads. Count the number of fixations he makes per line. Do his eyes ever backtrack to look again at a word already passed?

Exhibit Idea

Use sketches of the eye and its muscles. Make an eye model that can illustrate eye movements. Diagram the kind of movements the eye can make. Describe eye movements in reading. Devise a mirror setup so that eyes can be observed while reading.

Experiment 23

DOMINANT EYE

Apparatus: Cardboard with hole, cone-shaped cardboard funnel

Did you know you have a dominant eye just as you have a dominant hand? It is generally the eye you sight with.

With both eyes open, sight a distant object through a 1-inch hole in the center of a cardboard as shown in Fig. 23–1. Move the card-

Fig. 23–1. Hole in card will be lined up with distant object by using the dominant eye.

Fig. 23–2. Dominant eye will sight down the funnel to aim at a distant object.

board in to touch your face, keeping the distant object sighted. Which eye were you using?

You must hold the cardboard with both hands. Try the same thing with a rolled cardboard funnel (Fig. 23–2). Repeat each test several times. Do you always choose the same eye? Is your dominant eye on the same side as your dominant hand?

Your dominant eye by these tests is your sighting eye. Actually it is much more complex than this; generally other dominance tests are used in addition. The dominant eye probably leads in making eye movements. In reading, for example, the nondominant eye may lag and make fixational movements with less precision.

Exhibit Idea

Design an apparatus to test dominance by looking into it. Make sketches of eyes indicating sighting dominance.

Experiment 24

MUSCLE BALANCE OF THE EYES

Apparatus: Hand occluder, penlight, fixation spot

Place a small fixation spot on a distant wall. While you stare at the spot, cover one eye, then the other, with a strip of cardboard. Carefully observe the position of the spot.

Does it appear to jump from side to side? Up and down? Move diagonally as first one eye sees it, then the other? Whether it does or not will depend upon the basic muscle balance of your ocular muscles. This is a complex topic that can be but barely touched on here. You can, however, study a number of different subjects to demonstrate that not everyone has the same muscle balance.

When one eye is covered, it will move to a position determined by the tone of its muscles. It may turn in or up, even up or down a little or a great deal. It may not move at all. If your eyes do this, you will see the spot jump as you cover one eye, then the other. Actually, with fixations at a distance, little if any jump is expected.

Repeat the process while you aim your eyes at a near object such as a pencil held 16 inches away. Now you probably will see the object jump as your eyes are alternately covered. Does it move the same or opposite to the direction of the movement of the occluder? The optometrist would use the direction and amount of jump as a means of diagnosing the type of muscle balance.

You can also see eye movements of someone else under these conditions. The experimenter on the right in Fig. 24–1 watches the subject's eye movements as the occluder is alternated from one eye to the other.

Repeat these observations on a number of subjects to discover differing responses to these muscle balance demonstrations. You will see eye movements if you look very carefully and if you hold the fixation spot quite close.

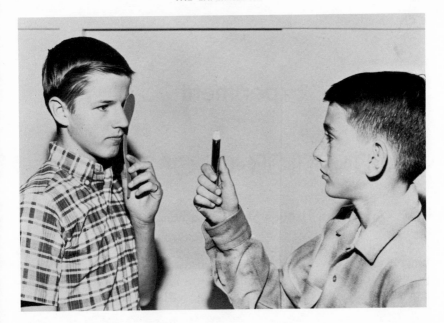

Fig. 24–1. Experimenter watches for eye movements as cover is moved from one eye to another.

Experiment 25

CONVERGENCE OF THE EYES

Apparatus: Fixation object on a handle or a penlight

Not only do your eyes move from side to side in order to keep images on the fovea, but they must also turn in or outward the appropriate amount for the distance of the object. To see a near object with each eye, they must aim inward—this is called *convergence*.

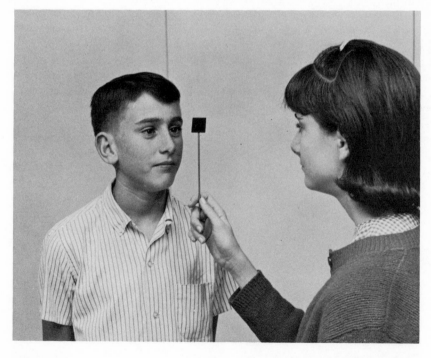

Fig. 25–1. Subject turns eyes inward to converge on object moved toward him.

Turning outward to look from a near to a far object is called *divergence*.

The skill with which eyes converge differs considerably from one person to another. You can measure the power to converge by having the subject follow a fixation object inward as you move it toward his eyes. (See Fig. 25–1.) Watch closely as his eyes turn inward. You can note when he reaches the limit of his convergence because one eye will suddenly let go and swing outward. Or he may tell you that he sees double when his eyes can no longer aim accurately.

Try this on a number of subjects. Some may converge all the way in to the bridge of the nose as close as shown in Fig. 25–2 or farther. Others may have great difficulty converging much closer than an ordinary reading distance. Generally the more convergence power, the better for visual performance. However, other compensating factors have to be considered and you must not jump to conclusion about results on any person.

You can also determine how easily the subject can converge by watching his eyes move as he looks back and forth from a near to

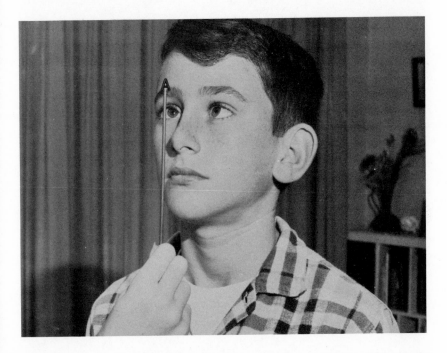

Fig. 25–2.   If object is held a little above subject's eye level, it will be easier to see his eyes converge.

a far object. Use a near object about 10 inches from his eyes, a distant one 10 or more feet away. Does one eye usually lead? How quickly can the subject converge? You will get the best result if the subject looks from one object to another on your command. Stand close to him and watch his eye movements very carefully.

Exhibit Idea

Make diagrams of the eyes and their muscles. Illustrate how the eyes coordinate together, converge, and diverge. Demonstrate with working models.

Experiment 26

PHYSIOLOGICAL DIPLOPIA

Apparatus: Fixation targets, strings

Your subject may have noticed on the previous experiment that when he looked at the far object, the near one appeared double. The reverse was also true.

This kind of double vision is called *physiological diplopia*. Vision is double because images fall on retinal areas that are not associated neurologically in such a way as to give rise to impressions coming from the same place in space. Rather they fall on retinal areas that do not "correspond" and thus the images appear in different directions.

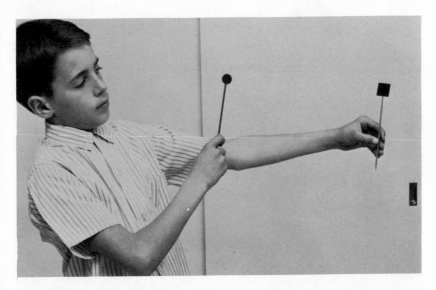

Fig. 26–1. When the subject looks at the square, the near circle appears double. The reverse is true when the circle is fixated.

This can be observed easily by use of two targets as shown in Fig. 26–1. Use a plain surface for a background. Hold the square as far as you can reach; the circle should be 8 or 10 inches from your eyes. Look at the square. Is the circle double?

Actually, many objects in space are double in everyday seeing but are not noticed because they are seen in side vision and given little attention. Besides, since their images are some distance from the sharp vision area of the retina, they appear blurred.

Fasten a string on a chair, or have someone hold the end, about 10 feet away (Fig. 26–2). Hold the other end on the tip of your nose. Fixate the string at its far end. The string close to you will appear double and thus you will see the string forming a V. Look carefully until you see this.

Now fixate along the string, progressively closer to you. The string will be single where you fixate, double elsewhere. It will appear as an X. As you fixate as close to you as possible, the string will again form a V, with its point toward you.

Some eyes do not see double easily. You may need to practice to get diplopia. This may be because one eye tends to suppress its

Fig. 26–2. The string appears single wherever it is fixated, double elsewhere.

vision. It usually is an indication of faulty two-eyed seeing, due to improper coordination of the two eyes. However, be cautious about making conclusions based alone on a demonstration such as this. Persistent suppression of vision in one eye, unless the cause is known by the subject, might indicate the need for an optometric analysis, however.

Fig. 26–3. Staring at a distant object causes an extra finger to appear to sprout between the two.

Figure 26–3 shows another interesting way to produce diplopia. Look at a far object. Hold your fingers as shown, about eye level and not quite touching. What do you see? Is there an extra finger floating between your real fingers?

Exhibit Idea

A modified string experiment could be set up for audience participation. Diagrams could explain diplopia and how the eyes see as one. Near- and far-sighting objects could illustrate double vision.

Experiment 27

BINOCULAR PROJECTION

Apparatus: Peg targets, large cardboard sheet

You have two eyes. Why do you only see one image? "Because the two images, one for each eye, are blended together into one." That is correct, but it is not as simple as it sounds. For one thing, when you do see double, as in the previous experiment, what determines the direction the images have in space? Do you use your right eye or left eye as the reference point?

You use neither real eye. A directional reference point must be two-eyed, in binocular vision. The two eyes work together as though you have a single eye, a single point from which all visual images are projected outward. This is such an effective principle that it even leads you to project some images into space where there is actually nothing at all. At the same time, you see nothing where the object really is under certain circumstances.

Set up a large cardboard sheet, about 4 feet long, on a table as shown in Fig. 27-1, or simply use the top of a long table. The subject sights on a distant vertical peg across the surface. Once the experiment has started, the subject's head must be held perfectly still.

First the subject closes his left eye, or the experimenter blocks it for him. A short blue peg is then moved until it appears perfectly in line with the distant green one. Notice that it is about 1 foot from the subject. Be certain that the head remains firmly fixed in position.

Next the right eye is closed. A short red peg is then positioned so that it appears in perfect alignment with the distant green peg.

Now the subject opens both eyes; they are of course both directed at the distant green peg. He will see three pegs directly in front of him. One is made up of a mixture of blue and red with the taller green peg sticking out above. This composite peg will appear on a

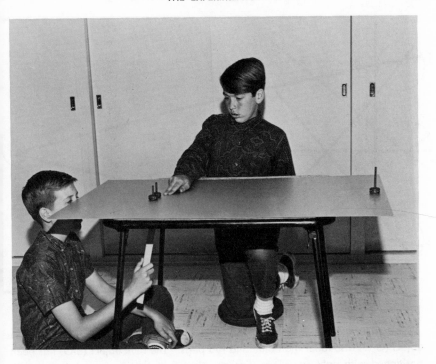

Fig. 27–1. Subject is pointing underneath sighting board where he thinks the images are. He cannot see the pointer, does it only by feel. Experimenter spots where subject indicates. He can lay paper under the pegs and actually mark with pencil where subject points.

midline from a point between his eyes and the green peg (Fig. 27–2). He can prove this by taking a ruler in one hand under the table and by touching the tip of the ruler exactly underneath where he sees the composite peg image.

Nothing really exists where the subject indicates that he sees the composite peg image. Check to be sure this is true. Yet it certainly appears to him that it is really where the image is. He also sees a single red and a single blue peg image. He can locate them in the same manner by tapping under the table with the ruler where they appear to be. The experimenter notes on the top surface where the ruler tips would come through.

If this is done very carefully, you can easily prove that he sees all three peg images, the composite one and the two singles, where there is no real peg at all. What has happened to the real peg? Again, if you observe very carefully, you will discover that when both eyes are open you see nothing there at all. Close one eye at

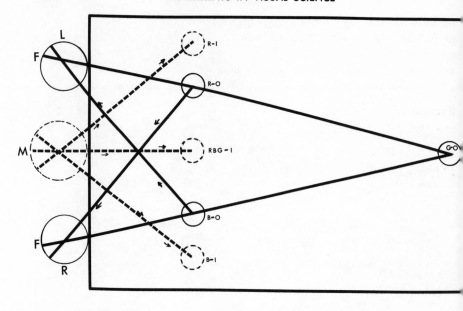

Fig. 27–2. The right eye (R) and left eye (L) are directed at the green object (G-O) also taller than blue and red pegs. The blue object (B-O) has been positioned with right eye alone (left eye closed) so that it appears in line with the green object. The red object (R-O) is lined up with the green object with the left eye alone (right eye closed).

The dotted circles represent where the images appear to be. M is the imaginary mental eye of binocular vision, a single eye that sees the images. Straight ahead it sees a composite red-blue-green image (RBG-I); this image is produced by real images falling on the fovea (F) of each real eye.

The so-called mental eye sees the blue image (B-I) in the direction shown. It belongs to the left eye, however. Close the left eye and see. Can you figure out why this is so? The red image (R-I) is seen to the left of the real object that created it. This image belongs to the right eye.

a time and you will see the images slide into the real pegs when you look with one eye.

In two-eyed seeing, you are using a directional reference point that is actually between your real eyes. With only one eye, you use that eye itself as a directional reference point; but with two you use an imaginary eye, shown in Fig. 27–2.

There are several other observations of this type that you can make with the sighting board and pegs. Place the single fixation peg close; adjust the other two at the end of the cardboard, one eye at a time so that they appear in line with the near one. See if you can find other ways to demonstrate binocular projection.

Exhibit Idea

Sighting boards and pegs could be used for demonstration. A sketch of projection principles, such as Fig. 27–2, would aid in explaining binocular projection.

Experiment 28

STUDIES OF BINOCULAR VISION

Apparatus: Cardboard square with opening and fixation line, series of fusion targets, cardboard strip

Each eye, of course, has its own retinal image. With both eyes open, you see only one image of objects upon which you fixate. What happens in binocular vision? Do you see only the image of one eye, parts of each one, or a blend of both? Actually all of those things can occur, depending upon the nature of each eye's image.

The results you will get in these experiments in binocular vision will partly depend upon the basic functioning of the subject's eyesight. For one thing, he must be able to converge adequately and control it. Some eyes will tend to suppress one image and favor the other. But the outcome is mostly dependent upon differences in the targets themselves. This is the principle to keep in mind: that the targets are so constructed to illustrate the blending process of binocular vision.

Examine Fig. 28–1. The cardboard held in hand has a 1½-inch square hole. Across the back of the opening is fastened a narrow strip of black paper. The subject's eyes must converge for the black line, and it must appear single throughout each observation.

The cardboard with the fixation line is moved in or out from the target propped up on the table until the two squares with crosslines appear to overlap perfectly. At this point, the subject is aiming at the fixation line on the opening in the cardboard he is holding. Inside the opening he sees fused images of the cross-lined squares.

Be sure you understand how this works. The right eye is aimed at the fixation line; through the hole it actually sees the square on the subject's left (Fig. 28–2). The left eye aiming at the fixation line is seeing the cross-lined square on the right. Check on this. Close one eye and see which square disappears.

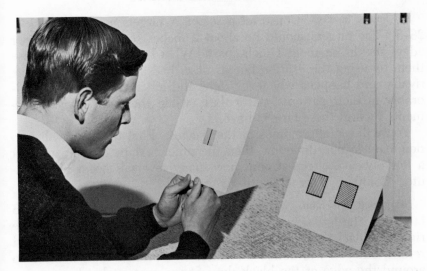

Fig. 28–1. The distance of fixation line and square aperture from the target must be adjusted until the position is reached where the two diagonal line targets appear exactly superimposed. Fixation must constantly be held on the black line of the hand-held cardboard.

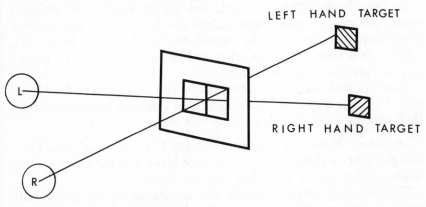

LEFT HAND TARGET

RIGHT HAND TARGET

Fig. 28–2. When the right eye aims at the central fixation line, it sees the left-hand target. The right-hand target is blocked off from the right eye by the right side of the cardboard. For a similar reason, the left sees only the right-hand target. When the lines of sight cross just the right amount, the targets appear superimposed.

The target images will be a little blurred. This is because the eyes are focused on the fixation line that is closer than the target. This makes no difference; the blur will not affect the result. With practice, young eyes especially may learn to clear up the targets and still keep the fixation line single.

(a) **Image Rivalry.** Construct a set of A targets as shown in Fig. 28–3. The targets should be about 2 inches square and the inner edges should be about 1 inch apart. What happens when you fuse them by using the fixation line as described above? This is image rivalry and happens whenever right and left images differ considerably in their patterns, particularly when there are crossing elements such as these targets have.

You will see alternations of the images. First the lines will predominate in one direction, then the other. At times, you will get a basketweave effect. Count how many reversals occur in 1 minute. Compare rates with other subjects.

(b) **Image Inhibition.** What happens when you use a set of B targets? The left side is red, or can be made from any color; the right is a black spot on a white background. The red may fade and return, but you will notice that there is a predominant white halo around the edge of the black dot. Sharp contrast borders on one image tend to inhibit that area of the image produced in the other eye. The red is inhibited by the black and white edge. Try it with different sizes of black dots and with other background colors.

(c) **Color Fusion.** The C targets are simply squares of different color. All sorts of color combinations can be used. If you can find two colors that are actually complements, they will blend into white when their images overlap in binocular vision. The proper red and green will make yellow.

You will find many interesting colors can be produced by blending. Colors actually fuse into something different binocularly from that which existed in either monocular image by itself.

(d) **Luster.** Make plain squares like the C targets with one black and the other a shiny red. Or one disk black and the other a shiny white. What do you see when they are fused?

This is called luster. Actually you are seeing the images of both eyes at the same time. The mind only accepts this as a sensible visual percept when the two images differ slightly in brightness and have a shiny appearance that permits them to be seen as a metallic luster.

(e) **Complete Image Fusion.** This is an area in which there is considerable difference of scientific opinion. What happens if the two images are identical? Suppose the right and left squares of target C are both blue. In binocular vision, which one is seen, or does it really look different from either or alone? There is no way this problem can be explored with simple apparatus.

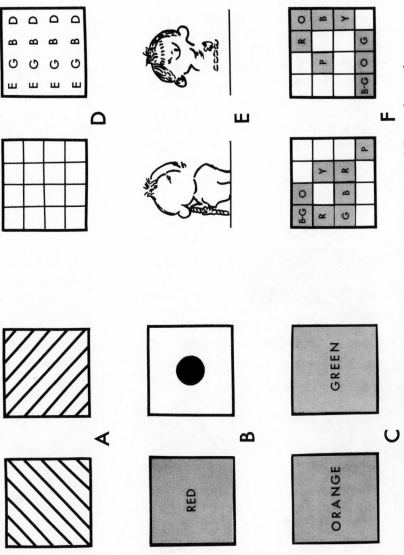

Fig. 28–3. Targets for observing binocular integration of targets differing for each eye.

Targets D, E, and F of Fig. 28–3 will make interesting ones to study. Predict before you try it what you expect to see. There are limitless target combinations with which you can experiment. The basic principles involved in binocular image blending are described above.

You may get some suppression of parts of the binocular image in targets like the D set in Fig. 28–3. Can you see all of the letters in the proper square? The little boy in the E targets should appear to be a complete figure, provided each eye contributes its proper image share. F is made up of squares of many colors. What effects does this produce?

How can you tell whether or not both eyes are seeing in ordinary usage? It is really quite easy. Refer to Fig. 28–4. While holding a 1-inch wide black strip of cardboard halfway between your eyes and reading a book or magazine, see if all the print is visible or part is blocked by the black bar. Close one eye. Can you see all the print? Try the other eye.

Fig. 28–4. If black bar does not block out any of the reading, both eyes are seeing and not suppressing.

Obviously you can see all the print only if both eyes are working and not suppressing vision. You can check on your binocularity for distance-seeing in the same manner. Hold the cardboard bar about 1 foot from your eyes. It appears double, of course, but does it block out any objects in your field of view? Why does it do so?

Exhibit Idea

The technique used here employing the fixation line in the square opening is a substitute for a stereoscope. These same targets could be used very nicely in a stereoscopic device. Simple ones can be obtained from optical companies or from an optometrist.

With a stereoscopic device, you could make a great many fascinating demonstrations. Invent your own targets to illustrate the kinds of binocular integration that this experiment has described. It would make a good audience-participation exhibit. It could be done without a stereoscope by the overconvergence principle, using a fixation point held closer than the targets. Separate look-in set-ups could be made for each kind of targets.

Experiment 29

STEREOSCOPIC DEPTH

Apparatus: Stereoscopic targets

There is one outcome of blending two images into one which is not covered in Experiment 28. It is a subject best studied by itself. This has to do with the depth effect produced when two images are slightly displaced with respect to each other, this produces stereoscopic depth.

Look at the two sets of black rings in Fig. 29–1. Do all of the rings look flat on the paper? Lay a pencil on the paper with its point exactly on the A between the top set of rings. During the entire demonstration, you must keep your eyes aimed at the pencil point. Now move the pencil very slowly toward your eyes. Remember to keep looking directly at its point (Fig. 29–2). You will actually see four sets of rings if you look carefully, but keep moving the pencil closer until you see three sets of rings. Stop and hold the pencil where this happens.

Pay attention to the sets of rings over the tip of the pencil, but do this without actually directing your eyes at the rings. Indirectly notice that now the small inner ring has floated off the paper closer to you than the large ring. Study it carefully. You may need to repeat it several times to see it. Adjust the distance between yourself and the target and the distance between the pencil and the rings until you can get the proper effect. The rings may look a little blurry but with practice you can clear them up. Try the same thing on the B set of rings. This time which ring looks closer?

Why does this happen? You will notice that R and L circles are a little different. The smaller rings are displaced slightly inward. By looking at the pencil held close to you, your right eye aims at the R circles, and your left at the L set of rings. This was the same thing you did in the previous experiment with the cardboard aperture. (See Fig. 28–2.)

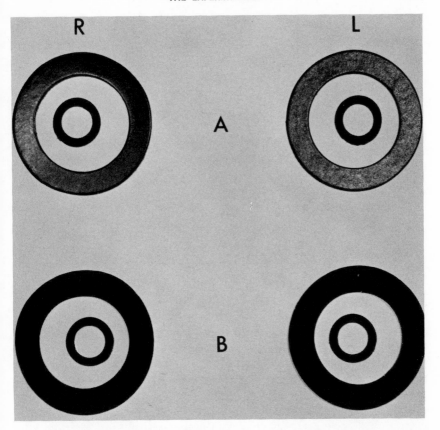

Fig. 29–1. The targets printed here can be used to demonstrate stereo-scopic depth. To make your own, draw them as shown; or for particularly effective ones, get cardboard cutout letters used in making signs. These can be obtained at art supply or sign painters stores. These were made from the letter O of different sizes. Space to whatever separation works best for you; this can be done easily with cardboard letters, which are movable on the paper.

Each eye sees a slightly different image and, when they are blended in the brain, a depth effect occurs. You are seeing two slightly different images as you do in a stereoscope. In fact, you could use a stereoscope for all targets used in the studies of binocu-lar vision and stereopsis.

The large ring targets of Fig. 29–3 produce a striking depth effect. Does it appear that you are looking into a tube?

If it is easier to use the cardboard square and fixation line, as in Experiment 28, you can view the stereoscopic targets that way,

Fig. 29–2. Pencil is moved toward the face until each set makes three rings; the center one, produced by an image in each eye, will have a depth effect.

using a circular opening. The big advantage is that the cardboard will block off the extra images you see when using the pencil to fixate.

Draw some patterns of your own. You can use different colors. Try squares, triangles, lines, and various other shapes. In constructing the targets, you must displace a part of the pattern with respect to the rest of it in order to get a depth effect. You can see how this was done by examining the targets in Figs. 29–1 and 29–3. It is possible to produce many fascinating depth effects, even with complex patterns. Let your imagination go to work.

Fig. 29–3. Notice that each ring is displaced a little inward; this creates the depth effect. In this kind of target, where right eye sees the left target and left eye sees the right one, the rings displaced inward will seem the farthest away. If you want the smaller rings, for example, to appear closer, displace them outward in constructing a target.

Exhibit Idea

Read the suggestions with Experiment 28. Stereoscopic effects could likewise be used for demonstration. With two projectors, you could produce stereoscopic depth effects with polaroid. You would need to study this. Each stereoscopic target must be projected through a polaroid film differently positioned. They must be viewed through polaroid filters so oriented that each eye sees only one target. This is the same principle illustrated here.

Experiment 30

DEPTH PERCEPTION

Apparatus: Adjustable peg device

You can test depth perception by a vertical peg device such as shown in Fig. 30–1. One peg is fixed in position halfway between the two ends. The other peg is mounted on a small block. The subject moves the left-hand peg back and forth by pulling the cords that run through a pulley at the back of its track.

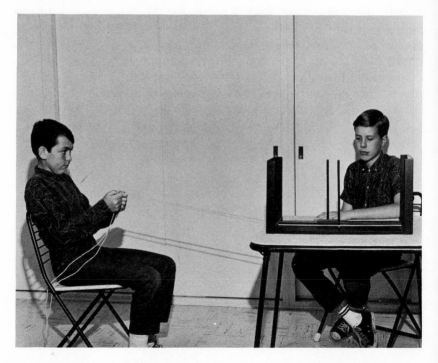

Fig. 30–1. Adjustable peg device for testing depth perception.

The subject looks through a rectangular opening in the front panel that enables him to see only the middle area of the pegs, not their tops nor bottoms and none of the track. The black pegs are viewed against the white back panel of the device.

The experimenter displaces the movable peg and asks the subject to adjust it until it appears to be exactly even with the fixed one. A metric system scale is mounted along the track of the movable peg and the position of the peg is noted each time that alignment is made. An average is taken for five settings. The subject should be seated at least 12 to 15 feet from the fixed peg.

This is only a demonstration of depth perception and should not be considered a valid test in itself, though a similar device is actually used for testing. The subject can check his alignment accuracy with both eyes together and each alone. Which way is better? He should not move his head from side to side while he is making the peg setting.

Exhibit Idea

Such a device could be used to demonstrate depth perception. Include a list or illustrations of other factors in depth perception such as image size, shadows, geometric perspective, intervening objects, apparent size (see illusion Fig. 34–11), and atmospheric haze.

Experiment 31

PULFRICH STEREO PHENOMENON

Apparatus: White thread, small button, dark lens or plastic

This is one of the most interesting experiments to perform. It is not well known. It seems like an illusion and in a sense it is. A depth effect is created when there really is no depth. Yet it is based on a very sound principle of stereoscopic depth perception.

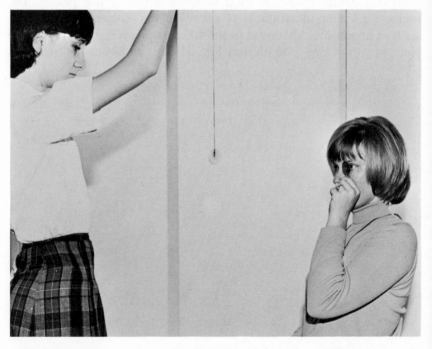

Fig. 31–1. Button on end of thread is swung pendulum fashion in a straight line. Subject sees it move in a circular manner with dark lens over one eye.

Fasten a white button about ¾ of an inch wide on the end of a piece of white thread. Have someone hold the thread so that the button can swing at the end like a pendulum. It is best to view it against a plain wall. (See Fig. 31–1.) While you stand several feet away, he should swing the button gently back and forth. Be certain he swings it in a perfectly straight line. Notice how it appears to be moving to and fro like a pendulum on the clock.

Now hold a sunglass lens over one of your eyes. Any plain sunglass will do, or even a piece of dark glass or plastic. However, it must cover only one eye. With the dark lens over one eye, look at the swinging button again.

Observe very carefully. Does the button look like it is swinging in a circle? When you see this, place the sun lens over the other eye. Does the button reverse itself and swing in the opposite direction? This is known as the Pulfrich Stereo Phenomenon.

How can this be explained? It is a matter of timing, speed, and how fast the eye sees. Since the length of time it takes light and dark images to reach consciousness is different, at any given instant the two images the brain receives for comparison come from slightly different retinal positions. This produces a depth effect just as images slightly displaced did so in Experiment 29.

Exhibit Idea

Along with other depth-perception demonstrations, this phenomenon would be very effective. A swinging object could be constructed in a box and a filter provided for the viewer to use.

Experiment 32

VON HORNBOSTEL'S CUBE

Apparatus: Stick cube

Make a hollow cube by gluing 12 toothpicks or wooden sticks together as shown in Fig. 32–1. Round toothpicks can be used. The effect works best if the sticks are painted a dull black.

It is best to make two squares first, let them dry, and then fasten them together with the remaining four wooden sticks. Attach a handle at one corner of the tube by gluing on a stick; it may help to steady it by tying the handle on with thread.

Hold the cube in front of you exactly as shown in Fig. 32–2. It is best to view it against a blank wall. The corner X must be pointing away from you and it must appear centered in the front side of the cube.

Close one eye and look steadily at the corner X. Suddenly you will see the cube appear to reverse and the corner X will look as though it is sticking out towards you. Now slowly twist the handle and you will see the cube appear to turn in the opposite direction. Wiggle the handle and you will see it create a weird effect.

It may take several trials to see it properly. Be sure the cube is positioned as shown. If it does not work, try a different background. It may help to move, tilt, and twist the cube a little. Keep at it until you see the effect. *It only works with one eye.*

This is known as the Von Hornbostel's cube illusion. The two eyes working together can see depth so well that they are not fooled. But one eye gets mixed up about which part of the cube is closer. This is one of the most interesting illusions known.

Exhibit Idea

Make a cube for display. Use it with other illusions and depth effects for an interesting exhibit.

Fig. 32–1. Performing Von Hornbostel's cube illusion.

Fig. 32–2. The corner X is inside the stick cube and away from the subject. Staring at the corner (without the letter) will cause it to reverse and appear to come forward. Then the cube is turned to get the illusion.

Experiment 33

SIZE CONSTANCY

Apparatus: Two sets of cardboard squares

Make the two complete sets of squares from black cardboard with the smallest measuring ½ inch on a side, each successive one being ⅛ inch larger. Starting with the smallest progressively to the largest, label the back of each set with numbers 1 through 25. Thus, the largest square will measure 3½ inches on each side.

One series of squares should be arranged (numbers down) in order on a table before the subject. (See Fig. 33–1.) The other series will be used by the experimenter who selects, unseen by the subject, a square that he presents to the subject at a distance of 3 feet from the subject's eyes. The card should be shown against a plain background and should be held on the edge and not be concealed in any part by the experimenter's hand.

The subject then points to the card in the series before him that he judges to be the same size. The subject should not see the number nor receive any clue or comment that might influence his selection. The subject should make a careful, but prompt, selection.

At the 3-foot test distance, the experimenter uses ten different squares, picked at random, covering a wide range of sizes. The same ten squares all unknown to the subject are used in the same way at 6 feet, 12 feet, and 24 feet. Some of the squares other than the ten squares should be used, but not scored so the subject does not learn any of the proper ones. The procedure is exactly the same: The experimenter holds up a square; the subject indicates which size he thinks it is by pointing to those in front of him.

The findings are recorded in a table like Fig. 33–2. In the left-hand column, in the space provided, put the number of the test squares you are using. As the subject makes his choice to match each number, record the number of the square he chooses. This is done for every test square used at every test distance. After all the

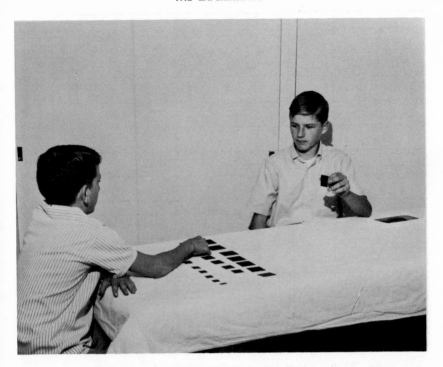

Fig. 33–1. Subject points to square that appears to match one held up by experimenter at each testing distance.

findings are made, calculate the difference and record in the proper column space. If the number of the square chosen by the subject is larger than the test square number, record the difference as a plus value; if it is smaller, give it a minus value.

For each test distance, calculate the total for the difference column. Add the plus values to each other. Add the minus values to each other. Calculate the difference and give the remainder the sign of the higher number. What do your totals show?

If the size that an object appears to have is directly related to the size of the retinal image it creates, each test object should appear only half the size at 6 feet that it did at three, half again as small at 12 feet, and once more reduced in size by half at 24 feet. If this were the way your subject selected squares to match those in front of him, he would have chosen squares a great deal smaller than the test square as the test distance increased. As a result, the sum of the difference at each increasing distance would have been a large minus number, and it would be larger at each greater distance.

No. of Test Squares	3 Feet		6 Feet		12 Feet		24 Feet	
	No. of Squares Chosen	Dif.	No. of Squares Chosen	Dif.	No. of Squares Chosen	Dif.	No. of Squares Chosen	Dif.
Total								

Fig. 33–2. Chart for recording results of size constancy.

On the other hand, if there were absolute size constancy—that is, the object looked the same size at every distance—the subject would have selected the proper match at each distance and the sum of the difference would have been zero. Because of the testing conditions, you may even get the same plus totals at some distances.

Things are commonly perceived to have a size representing a compromise between "constancy" and the influence of the size of the retinal image. Thus, you will probably get a sum of the difference values that increase slightly in minus values, or decrease in plus, as you progress from the 3-foot to the 24-foot testing distance. However, there are individual differences and responses will vary. Still, it will be easy to prove that the apparent size of a square as it is moved farther away certainly does not shrink at the same rate as does its retinal image size.

Exhibit Idea

Devise a setup similar to that shown in Fig. 33–3. The square rotated in the rectangle by the experimenter has a scale on the top that shows the "shape" of the retinal image, which is equal to the length of the rotated diagonal divided by the unrotated. See if you can figure out how to design such an experiment and test for shape constancy. It could be used for a class demonstration.

Fig. 33–3. Performing an experiment on the principle of shape constancy.

Experiment 34

OPTICAL ILLUSIONS

Apparatus: Drawings of illusions

The subject of optical illusions is a vast one indeed. There have been thousands of illusions produced, many on purpose, some by accident. The greatest challenge to you, the experimenter, will be to devise new ones. There are thousands of possibilities, variations of size, shape, distance, and direction. See how many you can construct by getting ideas from the ones that follow:

(a) **Reversible Figures.** Perhaps not exactly illusions, but certainly targets that produce a variable response are those that can be seen in different ways. Look at Fig. 34–1. Is it a vase or two profiles? Why does it reverse? It does so because it makes a "good" figure either way. As a vase or as profiles, it is a sensible image.

Fig. 34–2 has objects that reverse depending upon how you look at them. Part A particularly reverses very easily. See if you can make other drawings of boxes, cubes, funnels, and pyramids that will reverse.

Does the cube in Fig. 34–3 reverse? In Experiment 32, you made a three-dimensional cube that reversed. Draw four or five cubes on white paper. Now lightly shade one side of the cube—does that stop the reversal? Try the other sides, including the inside. Does that tell you anything about why they reverse?

(b) **Direction of Lines.** Some of the most common illusions, some known for centuries, are illustrated by Fig. 34–4. Such illusions consist of straight lines or regular circles or forms that do not appear straight or regular because of angles created by background shown by Figs. 34–5, 34–6, and 34–7.

You can produce your own line illusions. Do not merely copy these. Experiment carefully to see what effects you can produce. Change the background, the line angle; determine the influence

Fig. 34–1.

A

B

Fig. 34–2.

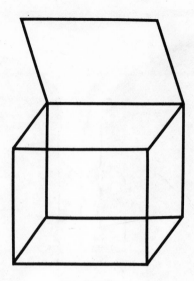

Fig. 34–3.

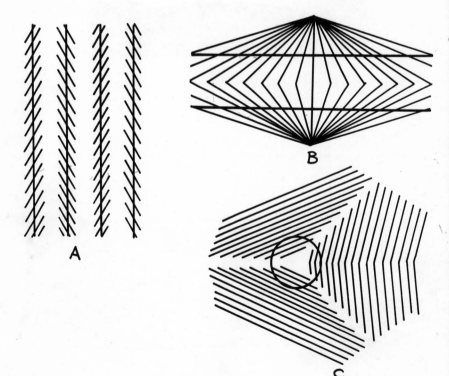

Fig. 34–4.

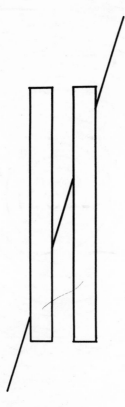

Fig. 34–5.

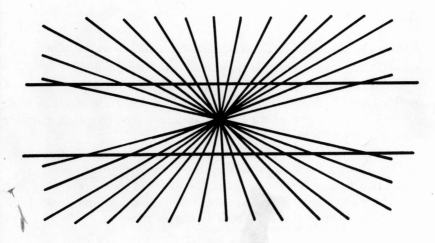

Fig. 34–6.

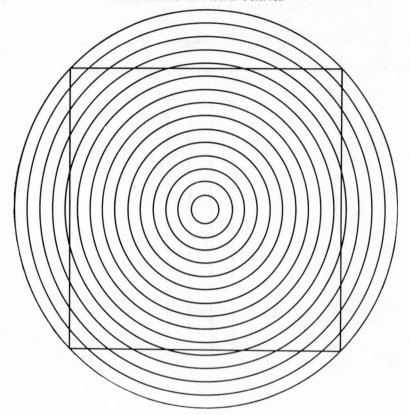

Fig. 34–7.

various changes will produce on regular figures. You could make a fascinating display of this type of illusion using colors.

(c) Size, Distance, and Length.   Figure 34–8 is an excellent example of this type of illusion. Cut equal-sized circles such as are A and B. See how you can change their apparent size by placing other figures around them.

Get your ruler out to check on the length of the lines in the circle in Fig. 34–9. Check each part of the bottom figure as well.

Cut two figures from cardboard the shape of the one in Fig. 34–10. Use two colors. Place one above the other. Which looks bigger? Now reverse them. Which is bigger now?

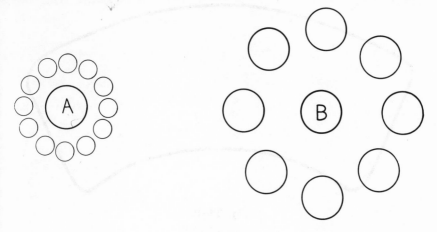

Fig. 34–8.

Fig. 34–9.

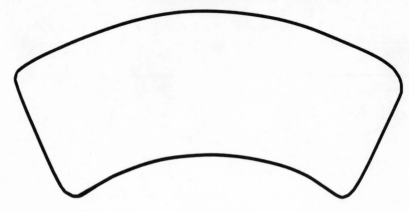

Fig. 34–10.

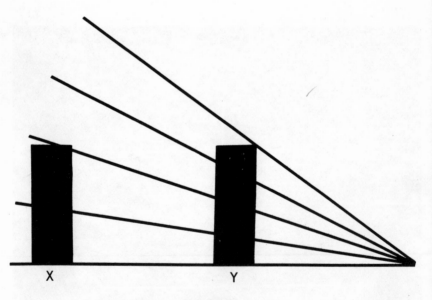

Fig. 34–11.

Make a diagram like Fig. 34–11. It should be about 12 to 15 inches long and 6 inches high. Cut two rectangles 3 inches and position as X and Y. Which is larger? Reverse them. Can you think of other illusions like this?

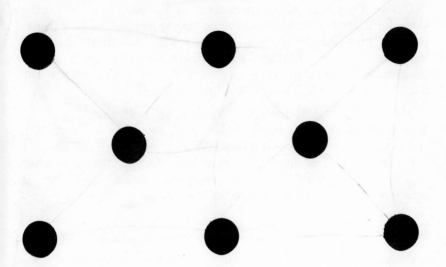

TEN SPOTS

Fig. 34–12.

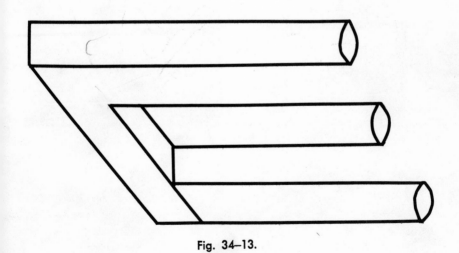

Fig. 34–13.

Did you know the large appearance of the moon on the horizon is an illusion? It is actually the same size as overhead. It is proved so by a photograph at each position. The next time the moon looms large on the horizon, stand where you can see it without obstruction. Notice its size. Now view it over a mask so you cannot see the ground. Does it still look as large?

(d) Groupings. Is it hard to convince yourself that Fig. 34–12 does not have ten dots because the words say there are ten? Can you compose other illusory groupings?

Figure 34–13 can hardly be classified. Lines, grouping, what? Where does the third leg go? Perhaps you can invent another design that will become as famous as this one.

Exhibit Idea

Prepare an interesting collection of illusions demonstrating as many effects as possible. Design some of your own. Make a study of other illusions in some of the reference readings to get additional ideas. You will find these particularly good for classroom demonstration or a science fair.

Experiment 35

MOTION EFFECTS

Apparatus: Pad of paper, dual light source, projectors or flashlights, spiral disk

Wave your finger in the air. Why does it appear to move? Its image sweeps across the retina while the rest of the retinal image is stationary. Follow your finger with your eyes and it still seems to move. In this instance, the background sweeps across your retina while the image of your finger remains in your fovea.

Figure appears to move, not background, no matter which is really moving. Your finger was the figure whether you looked at it or not. This figure-ground relationship is so powerful that it can create an illusion.

When your car stops at a red light, you may suddenly feel like you are rolling backward as a car next to you pulls forward. Yet your car is not moving. You and your car become figure, the other car becomes background; thus the apparent movement of your car.

Many motion effects occur, however, when there is no movement at all. Without this, there would be no moving pictures and no television movement. The movies, of course, are a series of still pictures, presented so rapidly that the visual mechanism fills in the space from one position of an object to another with movement.

Phi Movement

Make a sketch of a stick figure walking on the bottom page of a pad of paper. Put it near the edge of each page where it can be seen as you flip the pages with your finger. On each following page, make another sketch of the figure a little farther along the edge. As the edges are flipped quickly, the figure appears to walk.

You can produce a remarkable motion effect with two spots of light. Two flashlights will do, provided you can produce two spots

Fig. 35–1. Each projector produces a spot positioned a few inches apart; a wall or cardboard can be used for a screen. Here the subject is alternately covering the projectors to create a motion effect.

of light that are very much alike in size and brightness. Two projectors will work even better. See page 112 about use of projectors and flashlights for the experiments and how to produce spot images.

Direct two spots on the wall so that they are about 2 or 3 inches in diameter. They should slightly overlap at first; then, if your conditions are right, you will be able to separate them a foot or more and still get the effect. Get the spots as equal as possible in size and brightness. Now alternately cover one, then the other source, with a piece of cardboard at a rate rapid enough to make it appear as though the spots actually slide back and forth on the wall. (See Fig. 35–1.) You will need to experiment a little to get the best effect.

This is called *phi* movement. The images on the retina are stationary, but they change so rapidly that the space between them is filled in perceptually. This is the exact basis for the moving appearance of motion pictures.

Work with various targets, spots, even colors in the projectors. How far apart can they be? Try it with the room very dark. Is this the basis for motion you often see in electric signs?

Fig. 35–2. The Plateau Spiral. Box contains phonograph turntable motor.

Moving Aftereffect

Construct a disk of black and white, like Fig. 35–2. Mount it on a wheel so that you can rotate it. The one shown here is rotated on a 78 rpm. record player turntable. If your player operates at that speed, mount the disk on the turntable; you can look down on the disk as it spins. It can be mounted and turned by hand, or any variable speed motor can be used; however, the illusion will not occur if the speed is too great.

Stare steadily at the center of the disk while it is rotating. After half a minute, or a minute or more if necessary, look away at some object on the wall, or at your partner's face, in fact at any object. What happens? Reverse the direction of the disk so that it seems to turn from the inside outward. The object you fixate afterward should now appear to shrink in size. Does it? Try until you see this.

You can get the same sort of effect by staring at the rushing water of a waterfall, then looking at the nearby ground. Try that sometime. There is no completely satisfactory scientific explanation of this phenomenon.

Fig. 35–3. This large spiral, turned by hand, is a particularly effective design.

Exhibit Idea

Motion effects would make a striking demonstration. Design them so the audience can participate. Fig. 35–3 shows a particularly potent design to create an aftereffect.

Experiment 36

SUBTRACTIVE COLOR MIXING

Apparatus: Flashlight or projector light source, colored cellophane, plastic, or glass filters, water color paints

White light contains all of the wavelengths of the visible spectrum. Thus it contains all the hues the eye can see. Figure 36–1 is a color circle, all colors combined make white. It is possible to start with a beam of white light and subtract certain wavelengths, leaving a remainder that is dependent upon the nature of the subtracting substance.

(a) Subtraction with Filters. You will need a flashlight that is capable of producing a sharp, narrow, and, above all, a uniform beam in brightness. You can mask the beam by using a cardboard with a ¼-inch hole in the center. This may sharpen it enough. You may need to put a diffusing filter of paper or plastic over the flashlight to make the light uniform.

Any ordinary slide projector will work very well. It has a condensing system that will produce a sharp spot of light. You can punch a hole in a stiff cardboard cut to the size of the slides the projector accepts. Put this in the slide carrier and it will give the type of light spot needed (Fig. 36–2).

For subtracting filters, you can use colored cellophane, colored plastics, or colored glass. Best of all are gelatin filters. You can purchase Wratten filters in gelatin from a photography supply store or from scientific supply companies. These are excellent optically and can be used for the next experiment as well. These are almost essential if you wish to do precise color experiments. You should have a selection of colors throughout the spectrum.

Focus your flashlight or projector on a white or gray screen. Select a filter, hold it toward the light, and note its color. What

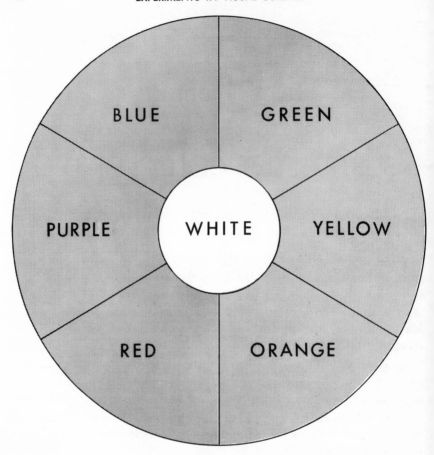

Fig. 36–1. Colors directly opposite each other on the color circle are complementary—that is, proper wavelengths make white.

Any color mixed with any other color, except its complement, will produce a color between the two; green and orange, for example, produce yellow; green and purple produce blue; red and yellow make orange, etc. Neighboring colors do likewise—produce a color between them; for example, blue and green produce a blue-green color, purple and red make a magenta. The exact color produced depends upon the amount of each individual color in the mixture.

Certain combinations of three colors also make white, and there are many such combinations. These sets of three are called primaries.

colors will it transmit? It will pass colors similar to its own color. What will it not transmit? These are the ones it will subtract from the white light. Try it.

Experiment with various combinations of filters. It is possible to make the spot black. What is true of the filters that do this?

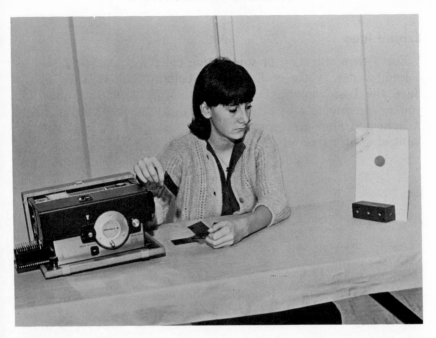

Fig. 36–2. Subtractive color mixing is done by starting with white light, holding filters in the beam to subtract certain wavelengths.

Why does the eye see no color? One filter subtracts certain wavelengths from the white; when a second filter is then placed over the remainder, it may filter out the rest of the light.

It is oversimplified here. Some filters subtract more wavelengths than others. Some transmit at both ends of the spectrum, for example. But generally, transmission is restricted to the region of the spectrum represented by the filter's own color.

(b) **Subtraction with Paints.** Get showcard colors, red, blue, yellow, green, white, and black. On a white paper, paint tiny color patches in groups. First use a touch of one color, then a touch of a second. Try all combinations possible.

Can you correctly predict the color you will get before you mix them? What is happening? The white light reflected from the paper before you add paint has some wavelengths subtracted from it by the substance of the paint material, by its pigment. Some wavelengths are absorbed.

Try combinations of three colors. What is happening now? Can you produce black? Mark as many hues as you can with two and three combinations. What does white or black do when added to a mixture? Lighten or darken? Yes, but why?

Exhibit Idea

For a demonstration of subtractive color mixing, you could use colored water. Cake or Easter egg coloring can be used to produce the basic colors. Poured together in various combinations you are producing subtractive mixtures just as with filters or paints. A light and filter arrangement also would make an interesting exhibit of subtractive mixing.

Experiment 37

ADDITIVE COLOR MIXING

Apparatus: Three light sources, flashlights, projectors, or color-mixing box, selection of colored filters, rotary device for color mixing

The color sensations that the eye produces depend upon the wavelengths it receives. In the previous experiment on subtractive color mixing, you started with white light and removed some wavelengths. The color produced depended upon the remainder.

Perhaps even more fascinating is the process of additive color mixing. In this method, different combinations of wavelengths are sent into the eye together. The resultant sensation is the sum of the action of the components.

(a) **Constant Light Sources.** You can only do this with multiple sources of light. To produce all the effects, you must have three sources. You will need to use an apparatus that makes it possible to control the wavelength of each source by itself and for all three to be superimposed in some way.

Three good flashlights may do, provided you can produce a good spot with them. The experiment does not give good results unless the spots from the sources are sharp and of uniform brightness.

Three small projectors are ideal. They need not be a good quality, nor all the same kind. Adequate projector sources can be purchased for a few dollars. They are useful in color mixing, in producing afterimages, creating some motion effects, and as a source in studying reflection and refraction described elsewhere.

Adjust the light sources so that the three spots overlap as shown in Fig. 37–1. In front of each source place one of the primary colors red, green, blue. These can be Wratten gelatin filters, glass filters, or even colored cellophane in proper colors. In securing the filters, if the information is available, be sure you obtain three

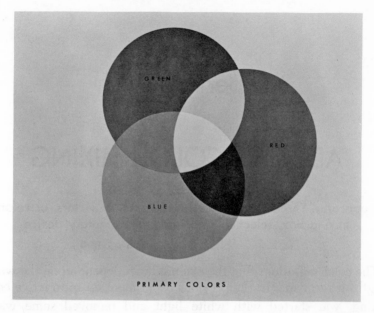

Fig. 37–1.   Additive color mixing by producing three colored spots on a screen.

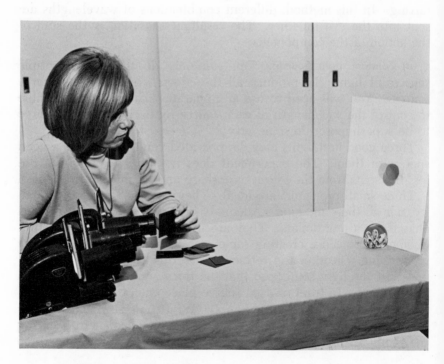

Fig. 37–2.   A triple projector setup is excellent for color mixing.

primaries. This is possible if you obtain them from a scientific supply source or a camera store. At the same time, get a selection of colors, violet, purple, orange, etc.

Experiment with as many different color mixtures as you have available. Hold the filters right over the projector lens (Fig. 37–2). You may need to change intensity of certain spots to get the best results. This can be done by adding neutral filters or a translucent plastic along with the filter in order to cut intensity. Even better, control the projection with a rheostat. You will need to try various combinations.

See if you can find two colors that are complementary. Together in proper intensity they should produce white. With cellophane or plastic filters, you may need several thicknesses to produce good results. Get the best white possible. Adjust intensities to get various additive hues.

(b) **Alternate Sources of Light.** You can also produce additive color mixtures by revolving disks with colored sectors so rapidly it is the same as if each color stimulus were constantly shining on the visual cells. This makes an excellent classroom demonstration and exhibit.

Fig. 37–3. Color-mixing device that houses motor whose speed is regulated by a rheostat control.

The best rotating device is one like that shown in Fig. 37–3. It contains a motor whose speed is controlled by a rheostat. Any simple motor-driven device will do. If it can be reversed, all the better, though this is not essential.

Rotation of the disk can be done by a hand-driven device. You could construct one with an egg beater arrangement. Even the electric type would work. Tops of color spun on the floor will even produce the effect. Invent something that will serve your purposes.

Figure 37–4 shows patterns of color disks that can be used on the mixer. You can paint the colored sectors with showcard paints, or any paints. They can be made of colored cardboards or papers. You will need to experiment to find three that are exact primaries. There are any number of patterns you can create for the disk.

The light falling on the disk is important. You can try various sources—lamps, room light, incandescent and fluorescent source, as

Fig. 37–4. Color-mixing disks can be made of various patterns and color combinations.

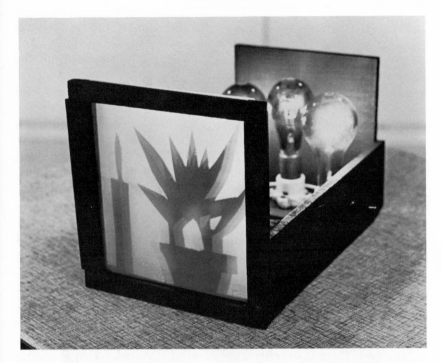

Fig. 37–5. Red, green, and blue bulbs in the back make triple colored shadows of cardboard silhouette mounted several inches back of front screen.

well as light from the window. You will not actually get a white, only a gray, which is white of low intensity.

There are a vast number of combinations possible. Use various colors, patterns, and sector sizes to produce as many hues as you can. Make a list of as many complementary colors as you can produce. How many primary combinations do you think there are? How many complementary pairs?

Exhibit Idea

Additive color mixing is a natural for a demonstration. Color wheels and projected colors both can be adapted very easily to an exhibit. You can build a color box with lights projected from behind to produce a pattern on the front surface like Fig. 37–1. Simultaneous contrast effects (Experiment 20) can also be produced with this.

Figure 37–5 is a colored shadow box that makes an attractive display.

Experiment 38

SUBJECTIVE COLOR

Apparatus: Special black and white disk designs

Simultaneous contrasts of color, whether by double projector devices, colored papers, and gray squares, or the vivid color effects by the device shown in Fig. 20–5, are purely subjective. They cannot be photographed. Experiment 20 also deals with subjective color effects. Induced color effects are brought about somehow by the electrochemical process of the visual system. How it actually occurs is not understood.

However, there is another kind of subjective color that is unique unto itself. It is produced from black and white stimuli alone. Though this effect was discovered over a century and a half ago, it still cannot be fully explained. It will be interesting to see if you get the same results on all observations. Remember this is purely subjective color.

The device in Fig. 38–1 has a variable speed motor, which is even reversible. The disk is rotated at differing speeds until color effects are produced when the disk is observed a few feet away. However, an electric motor is not necessary; it can be done with a disk rotated by a hard crank, or even a spinning top.

The colors produced depend upon the disk pattern. Figure 38–2 shows a few possibilities. There is almost no limit to the patterns possible; some you will find are more effective than others. The best colors will be seen at certain disk speeds. It may help to direct light upon the disk as it rotates. What happens if you reverse the disk direction? You will find it almost necessary to stop the spinning to convince yourself that the disks are really only black and white and not colored at all.

Exhibit Idea

Demonstration of subjective color is one of the most attractive exhibits you can make. The same device can be used for additive color mixing. See Experiment 37.

Fig. 38–1. Apparatus for producing subjective color effects.

Fig. 38–2. Disk patterns particularly effective in creating subjective color.

Experiment 39

"OP" ART

Apparatus: Art designs

Op Art, it is said, "attacks the eye." Actually it is a design or pattern that creates so-called optical effects. In a sense, op art is an illusion. It may visually appear different from the physical object, pattern, or design. Any figure that generates a perceptual response is optical art.

The op art may create a feeling, a sense of confusion, or one of orderliness. It may appear to move. It may create color effects. Whether or not "optical" is the proper name to apply to such art is a question. But it certainly is visual. It may even be emotional in that it relates to the mind's attempt to make sense of what it sees.

Most any pattern of squares, circles, dots, forms, and lines, whether in colors or black and white, is op art. It is particularly effective if there is some distortion of perspective, while intricate details add to the effects as well. Yet, regularity of pattern is also op art. For example, Fig. 18–2 is op art; in color it produces a powerful sensation of movement.

Figures 39–1, 39–2a, 39–2b, 39–2c were done by well-known artists. Certain feelings and emotions are created by certain styles. Some pieces of op art have sold for high prices. Some are hanging in famous galleries. In the last few years, there has been worldwide interest in op art.

You can make your own op art. Look at some of the illustrations. There are no rules, no style to follow; the more unique, the better. There are four ways to produce op art:

(a) **Freehand.** Notice Fig. 39–3. A pattern like this can be made with art tape, or line drawings. Perceptual effects can be made with any kind of geometric patterns, preferably with some regu-

Fig. 39–1.   A serigraph by Vasarely entitled "Metagalaxy." (Courtesy of The Pace Gallery, New York.)

Fig. 39–2a.   A painting by Jeffrey Steele, entitled "Fred Maddox—Baroque Experiment." (Courtesy of Grabowski Gallery, London.)

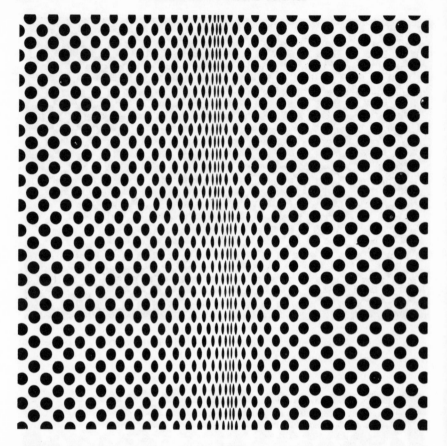

Fig. 39–2b. A painting by Bridget Riley, entitled "Fission." (Collection of Philip Johnson, New York.)

larity, but still a sense of confusion that "attacks the eye." There is no limit to what can be done; Figure 39–3 is only to give you an idea of a basic approach.

(b) **Photographically.** Figure 39–4 was made by photographing Fig. 34–7. A good sharp black and white negative was then exposed three times in the enlarger on the same sheet of photographic paper. On each exposure, the image was slightly reduced in size and displaced in position. Figure 18–2 was photographed and used to produce Fig. 39–5 by double exposure in the enlarger.

It is possible to put two negatives in the enlarger at the same

Fig. 39–2c. "Fall" by Bridget Riley was created intuitively and without recourse to science or mathematics. (Reproduced by courtesy of the Trustees of the Tate Gallery, London.)

time. This is how Fig. 39–6 was created. One negative had a ring pattern; the other, a series of diagonal lines. With patterns on film negatives, you can produce an endless variety of art pieces.

(c) **Mechanical Devices.** An amazing variety of patterns and designs can be produced by devices made for this purpose. Figure 39–7, which was produced by an apparatus called The Magic Designer, is an example. Such devices can be purchased in hobby and toy stores.

(d) **Moiré Patterns.** The Edmund Scientific Co. produces a kit for making Moiré Patterns. Figure 39–8 shows one produced by it.

Fig. 39–3. Freehand op art.

Fig. 39–4. Photographic op art.

Fig. 39–5. Photographic op art.

There is a great deal more to it than producing visual patterns, but it can be used for this as well. The kit provides you with enough materials to make many optical designs.

Exhibit Idea

The field of op art is limitless. There is room here only to make brief suggestions about how to produce and develop it. You can experiment and create your own methods and styles. You could make a fascinating display of op art using both black and white and color.

Fig. 39–6.　Photographic op art.

Fig. 39–7.　An op art pattern produced by a mechanical drawing device.

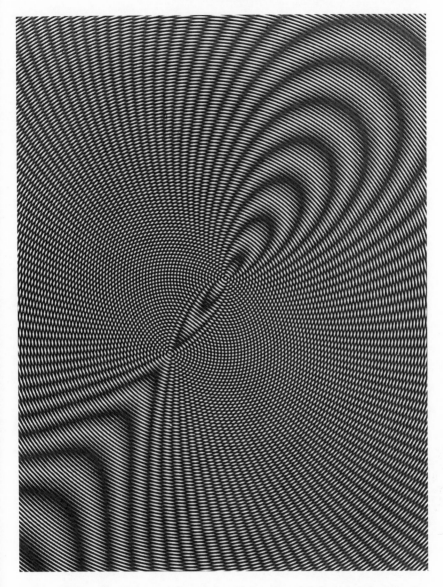

Fig. 39–8. Illustration produced by Moiré Kit of Edmund Scientific Co., Barrington, N. J.

Glossary

ACCOMMODATION—the act of focusing the eye.

AFTERIMAGE—a visual sensation that continues after the original stimulation has ceased.

ANGLE OF INCIDENCE—the angle a light ray makes with "the normal" as it proceeds toward the surface of a substance.

ANGLE OF REFLECTION—the angle a light ray makes with "the normal" after reflection from a surface.

ANGLE OF REFRACTION—the angle a light ray makes with "the normal" after refraction by a surface.

AQUEOUS HUMOR—a watery fluid filling the space between the cornea and lens.

ASTIGMATISM—refractive condition in which there is no point focus but rather two focal lines.

BINOCULAR VISION (two-eyed vision)—seeing with both eyes.

CANAL OF SCHLEMM—the space through which aqueous humor flows out of the anterior chamber.

CHEIROSCOPE—a stereoscope with a drawing platform.

CHOROID—a layer of tissue and blood vessels that supplies nourishment to the inner eye.

CHROMATIC ABERRATION—failure of an optical system to focus light of different wavelengths (different colors) exactly together.

CHROMATIC DISPERSION—the breaking up of white light into the colors of the spectrum.

CILIARY MUSCLE—a muscle inside the eye that enables it to change focus.

COMPLEMENTARY COLORS—any two colors that when mixed in proper proportion will produce white.

CONCAVE LENS—a diverging lens, the type used to correct nearsightedness, also called a minus lens.

CONE—retinal nerve cell specialized for visual acuity and color vision.

CONVERGENCE—the turning of the two lines of sight toward each other to aim at an object.

CONVEX LENS—a converging lens, the type of lens used to correct farsightedness, also called a plus lens.

CORNEA—transparent layer at the front of the eyeball, protective and refractive in function.

CRYSTALLINE LENS—the lens of the eye.

DARK ADAPTATION—the adjustment of the eye to low levels of illumination.

DIOPTER—a unit of lens power. A one diopter lens has the power to bring parallel rays of light to a point focus at a distance of 1 meter from the lens. Thus, the formula is: $\text{Diopter} = \dfrac{1}{\text{focal length in meters}}$ For example: a +3.00 lens is a plus lens, a converging lens of three diopters. Negative lenses, diverging lenses, are expressed with the minus sign.

DIPLOPIA—double vision, seeing two images when there is actually only one object.

DIVERGENCE—the turning away from each other of the two lines of sight as in looking from a near to a far object.

EMMETROPIA—a refractive condition of the eye; when the eye is completely relaxed, distant objects are in focus on the retina.

ENTOPTIC—from within the eyeball, used to refer to visual sensations created by objects, such as tissue cells that cause shadows to fall on the retina.

ERROR OF REFRACTION—*see* Refractive Error.

EXTRAOCULAR MUSCLES—the muscles that attach to the outside of the eyeball and direct its movements.

FARSIGHTEDNESS—*see* Hyperopia.

FIELD OF VIEW—*see* Visual Fields.

FIXATION—the act of aiming the eyes or an eye at a specific spot.

FOVEA—small area in the center of the retina that produces sharpest vision.

FUSION, MOTOR—the process of moving the eyes so that the image of a common object falls on corresponding retinal areas.

FUSION, SENSORY—the process that blends the two images, one from each eye, into a single mental image.

HOROPTER—locus of points seen singly with any given distance of fixation.

HYPEROPIA—when completely relaxed, the refractive power of the eye is too weak for good focus of distant objects; however, vision may be kept clear by accommodation. Also called Farsightedness.

INDEX OF REFRACTION—the ratio of speed of light in air to speed in a particular substance.

IODOSPIN—a light-sensitive chemical thought to be present in the retinal cones.

IRIS—the colored diaphragm that moves to control the amount of light entering the eye.

JUMP FIXATIONS—movement of eye from one object to another, also called saccadic movements.

LINE OF SIGHT—line along which the eye aims in fixating an object.

MONOCULAR VISION—one-eyed vision; seeing with one eye.

MYOPIA—refractive power of the eye is too strong for good focus of distant objects; however, it may see near objects clearly. Also called Nearsightedness.

NEARSIGHTEDNESS—*see* Myopia.

OBJECTIVE FINDINGS—a finding result, or change witnessed in external events or objects apart from one's self-consciousness or feelings.

OCCIPITAL LOBE—the posterior or back portion of the brain, composed of right and left halves, seat of the primary visual centers.

OCULAR MUSCLES—the muscles that move and focus the eye.

OP ART—a design or pattern that creates so-called optical or visual perceptual effects.

OPTIC DISC—area of the retina where nerve fibers leave the eye; contains no visual cells and thus produces a blind spot.

OPTIC NERVE—collection of nerve fibers from the optic chiasma to the lateral geniculate body.

OPTICAL INFINITY—generally taken to be any distance greater than 20 feet, light rays from any source at optical infinity travel parallel to each other.

OPHTHALMOSCOPE—an instrument used to examine the inside of the eye.

OPHTHALMOMETER—an instrument used to measure the refracting power of the cornea.

ORTHOPTICS—another name for visual training, particularly in cases of crossed eyes.

PATHOLOGY—the study of disease and abnormalities, including those of the eye.

PERCEPTION, VISUAL—the process of interpreting changes in the environment through the visual senses.

PERIPHERAL VISION—vision that is not foveal nor central but rather around the spot fixated.

PHI MOVEMENT—an apparent motion effect produced by successive images.

PHYSIOLOGY—the study of body functions.

PHYSIOLOGICAL DIPLOPIA—the normal doubling of objects, which, because they are beyond or closer than the plane of regard, create images on noncorresponding retinal areas.

PHYSIOLOGICAL OPTICS—the science of vision, encompassing all of the physical, physiological, and psychological factors involved.

POWER (LENS POWER)—the strength of a lens; its ability to focus light. Power is expressed in diopters.

PRESBYOPIA—decreasing ability, due to age, of the eye to focus for near objects.

PRIMARY COLORS—any three colors that when mixed in proper proportion will produce white.

PRISM—a wedge-shaped piece of glass that bends light but does not bring it to a focus.

PUPIL—the aperture in the iris through which light enters the eye.

PURSUIT MOVEMENT—the act of fixating a moving object.

REFRACTION—the bending of light as it travels between substances of different densities.

REFRACTIVE ERROR—expression of how the eye fails to bring parallel rays of light to exact focus on the retina.

REFLECTION—the return of light or sound waves from surfaces.

RETINA—the inner lining of the eye containing the visual receptors and many connecting nerve cells.

RHODOPSIN—a light sensitive chemical in the rods of the retina; also called Visual Purple.

ROD—retinal nerve cell specialized for detecting dim light.

SCLERA—the tough outer covering of the eye.

SIMULTANEOUS CONTRAST—contrast effects produced by interaction between parts of a retinal image.

SIZE CONSTANCY—a tendency for objects to be perceived as having a constant size regardless of the retinal image they produce.

SPATIAL LOCALIZATION—the ability to locate objects relative to other objects in the visual field.

SPECTRUM—visible spectrum is that range of wavelengths of light that is capable of producing visual sensations.

STEREOPSIS—one of the factors contributing to depth perception which is due to the eyes receiving slightly disparate images.

STEREOSCOPE—a device that permits images to be presented to each eye independently.

STEREOSCOPIC DEPTH PERCEPTION—see Stereopsis.

STIMULUS—an environmental change or factor, such as a spot of light, which causes a response in a sense organ, such as the eye. Thus, any object producing a retinal image is a stimulus.

STRABISMUS—a term for crossed eyes.

SUBJECTIVE COLOR—color entirely dependent upon the way the eye functions and one that cannot be produced photographically.

SUBJECTIVE FINDINGS—personal reaction relating to performance, one's own feeling, and experience.

TONOMETER—an instrument used to measure the fluid pressure inside the eye.

VISUAL ACUITY—a measure of the clearness or sharpness of vision.

VISUAL FIELD, BINOCULAR—that area of space visible with two eyes.

VISUAL FIELD, MONOCULAR—that area of space visible with one eye alone.

VISUAL TRAINING—the process of re-education of visual habits.

VITREOUS HUMOR (Vitreous Body)—the jelly-like substance filling the vitreous chamber.

Bibliography

BRAGG, WILLIAM. *The Universe of Light*. New York: Dover Publications, Inc., *ca.* 1940.

Collier's Encyclopedia. 24 vols. New York: Collier-Macmillan Library Service, 1965.

Encyclopedia Americana. 30 vols. New York: American Corp., 1965.

Encyclopaedia Britannica. 24 vols. Chicago: Encyclopaedia Britannica, Inc., 1965.

GREGG, JAMES R. *The Story of Optometry*. New York: The Ronald Press Co., 1965.

GREGG, JAMES R., and HEATH, G. C. *The Eye and Sight*. Boston: D. C. Heath & Co., 1964.

McGraw-Hill Encyclopedia of Science and Technology (ed.-in-chief: William H. Crouse). 15 vols. New York: McGraw-Hill Book Co., 1960.

MOORE, SHIRLEY (ed.). *Science Projects Handbook*. Washington, D.C.: Science Service, Inc.

Nature and Science

Science News Letter

Scientific American

TOLANSKY, SAMUEL. *Optical Illusions*. New York: The Macmillan Co., 1964.

Van Nostrand's Scientific Encyclopedia. 3d ed. Princeton, N.J.: D. Van Nostrand Co., Inc., 1958.

WOLF, THOMAS H. *The Magic of Color*. New York: Odyssey Press, 1964.

Index